Text Written by

Derek Holton
Professor of Mathematics
University of Otago
Dunedin, New Zealand

Problems Compiled by

Frank Rachich
Ingersoll, Ontario, Canada

Materials Revised and Edited by

Edwin Anderson
Vice-President, Waterloo Mathematics Foundation
University of Waterloo, Waterloo, Ontario, Canada

and

Ronald Dunkley
Director, Centre for Education in Mathematics and Computing
University of Waterloo, Waterloo, Ontario, Canada

PROBLEMS
and
how to Solve them
Volume 2

The CENTRE for EDUCATION in MATHEMATICS and COMPUTING
Faculty of Mathematics
University of Waterloo
Waterloo, Ontario, Canada
1997

Published by
The CENTRE for EDUCATION in MATHEMATICS and COMPUTING
Faculty of Mathematics
University of Waterloo
Waterloo, Ontario, Canada

Telephone: (519) 885-1211, extension 3030
Fax: (519) 746-6592

Canadian Cataloguing in Publication Data

Holton, Derek Allan, 1941-
  Problems and how to solve them : volume 2

ISBN 0-921418-12-4

1. Mathematics—Problems, exercises, etc. I. Anderson, Edwin. II. Dunkley,
Ronald G. III. Rachich, Frank. IV. University of Waterloo. Centre for Education
in Mathematics and Computing. V. Title.

QA43.H645 1997   510'.76   C97-932201-4

Printed by Graphic Services, University of Waterloo

Foreword

This book, written for students in senior secondary schools and for their teachers, is also intended for others interested in mathematics at this level. There are many publications aimed at the advanced problem solver. There is not much easily readable material for the student who is not ready for (or necessarily interested in) olympiad level tests and who wishes to know more of the background of the subject, how to attack good problems, and where a given topic might be leading.

These are important points. Indeed, they are the core of the discipline. How can one expect students to be interested in the subject if they have no idea where it comes from or where it is going?

This material then, is radically different from most other problem-solving texts. The dialogue, written by Professor Derek Holton of Otago University, Dunedin, New Zealand, aims to provide this information. The writing is personal and simple, and will give the reader a clear feel for the subject. The problems are compiled from Canadian Mathematics Competitions, supplemented by others created by Mr. Frank Rachich, a retired secondary school teacher in Ingersoll, Ontario. The material has been revised and edited by Edwin Anderson, retired Professor at the University of Waterloo, Waterloo, Canada, and Ronald Dunkley, Director of the Centre for Education in Mathematics and Computing, at the University of Waterloo.

Students wishing to use the material to best advantage will note that there are exploratory exercises in each chapter, to be done while reading the text. At the end of each chapter is a set of problems. If difficulty is encountered, hints for solving the more challenging problems are given before the solutions. These solutions should be accessed only after discussion with fellow students, teachers, and others (following use of the hints), proves fruitless.

There is sense in comparing your solutions with those provided. This will allow you to improve your presentation.

It is strongly recommended that students form study groups of three or four persons. Only by discussing ideas and approaches to problems can we improve our problem-solving skills. We urge that readers pay particular attention to the advice offered throughout the text. It is good, simple, and applicable.

We are especially grateful to Bonnie Findlay, University of Waterloo, for the many hours she spent in typesetting the manuscript and preparing the diagrams. Her patience and perserverance was extremely valuable to us. We also wish to thank Patty Mah, University of Waterloo, for the design of the cover and, in addition, we want to acknowledge the work done by Leanne Kirk and Lenette Grant in typing the material prepared by Professor Holton in New Zealand.

We trust that readers will derive pleasure and growth from their use of the text. Possibly some will feel sufficiently excited that they will pursue a university career in this most exciting and profitable (in career opportunities) subject.

Edwin Anderson
Ronald Dunkley
September, 1997

Contents

Chapter 1   An Introduction to Problem Solving

1.1   *Mathematics*

"A long while in the future and not so far away, the small planet Thrae revolved around its sun. The planet was ruled by a single mighty Emperor who dictated the history, both past and present, of the once noble planet."

"One of the Emperor's most insidious inventions was the Math Police. I cannot describe their power and purpose. But I can recognise them. They all have the mathmark on their forehead. The mathmark consists of six circles arranged three to each side of an equilateral triangle. In each circle is a single digit from 1 to 6."

"This by itself is not unusual for many citizens of Thrae have such a mark. What distinguishes the Math Police is that the sum of the numbers on each side of the triangle is the same, and each Math Police person has a distinct sign."

The above is part of a message sent via the Internet. The balance of the message was of such grave importance that it has been censored by the major powers. What you see in the message is all I could read before my system crashed.

It occurs to me though that it might have significant ramifications if we know what mathmarks the Math Police have. It might be nice to know how many of them there were, too. Do we have enough information to do this?

When you cut through all the rubbish above, what is it we're actually trying to find out? How do we go about finding the mathmarks?

First off, what does the basic mark look like? I think Figure 1 gives a pretty good idea of the fundamental shape. All I have to do is to find how to fit in the numbers 1 to 6.

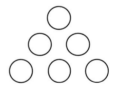

Figure 1

It seems to me that there are a number of ways of doing this. The first thing that comes to mind is to throw in values and hope for the best. Here's one in Figure 2.

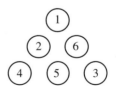

Figure 2

Is that a mathmark? What are the conditions for a mathmark? Six circles; arranged three to the side of an equilateral triangle; the sum of the numbers on each of the equilateral triangle's sides is the same.

$1+2+4 = 7$, $1+6+3 = 10$. Ah! Not a mathmark. I've got to make sure that all sides have the **same** sum. How can I do that? It might be possible to get the answer by guessing. Is there a more systematic way?

Exercises
1.   Before you start calculating, how many mathmarks do you think there are? Perhaps 10 or 20 or 100 or 1000 or ...?
2.   Can you find some mathmarks? Can you find **all** mathmarks?

If I think logically about this problem, it seems to me that I might put the big numbers, 4, 5 and 6, into the corners. Then I should be able to balance out the sides with the small numbers. In Figure 3(a), I've put the big numbers in the corners.

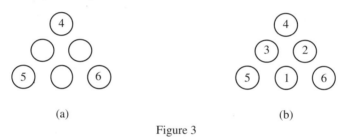

(a)   (b)

Figure 3

Now the bottom side already adds to 11 and it has the biggest possible sum so far. In order to balance up the three sides, I'd better put the 1 in the middle bottom circle. That gives me a side sum of 12. I automatically require 2 to the right and 3 to the left. I've found my first mathmark!

Is this the only mathmark? Is it possible to find other mathmarks given that we've got one? It is a bit too early to answer these questions. However, with some problems once you've got one solution you can use it to find another.

Now hang on here! I just got Figure 3(b) by talking about the **largest** numbers. What if I put the smallest numbers into the corners? Can I then balance up the sides with the biggest numbers?

Figure 4(a) is the start I need. What do you know? Figure 4(b) gives me another mathmark!

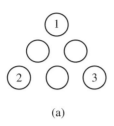

(a)

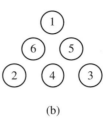

(b)

Figure 4

Exercises

3.   Have I got the only two mathmarks in existence?
4.   Suppose we drop the restriction that all mathmarks have equal sums on all sides. How many mathmarks are there now?

It occurs to me that there is a sure way to do this problem. Use a computer! There are not that many ways (by computer standards) of putting the numbers 1 through 6 into those rotten little circles. All my program has to do is to drop each of the numbers systematically into the circles and then check the side sums. That shouldn't be too difficult a program to write.

So far we have two different mathmarks from Figure 3(b) and Figure 4(b). They are different because their side sums are different.

But Figure 3(b) can be rotated about an axis of symmetry through the centre of the triangle and perpendicular to its plane. Doing this first by 120° and then by 240° gives two more mathmarks. But there are also three axis of symmetry in the plane of the triangle and through a vertex. Rotating through 180° gives us another mathmark for each axis of symmetry. Hence there are six mathmarks that can be obtained from each of Figures 3(b) and 4(b). So we have twelve mathmarks so far. In the diagram below I show the six mathmarks derived from Figure 3(b).

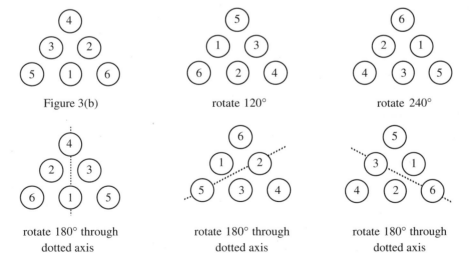

Figure 3(b)   rotate 120°   rotate 240°

rotate 180° through   rotate 180° through   rotate 180° through
dotted axis   dotted axis   dotted axis

But it's always nice to be able to reduce searches. What other things can I do to reduce the number of potential mathmarks? Can I use the side sum in any way? What is the biggest side sum a mathmark can have? What is the smallest? What are all the ones in between?

Now, we can't have a side sum made up of $4+5+6$ (Why?) However, we can put 1 with the two biggest numbers to get $12 = (1+5+6)$. I've already got a side sum of 12 (Figure 3(b)).

Reversing this, the smallest sum we can make is $1+2+3$ but 6 has to be in some side sum. Hence the smallest side sum we could hope for is $1+2+6$. And Figure 4(b) has given us one of them.

Can we get side sums of 10 and 11? Try it.

Hang on! Now I know about side sums, I can just write down all possible combinations of three numbers that add to that sum and try to fit them together to make the mathmark.

Hey, this might give me a way of finding how many mathmarks there are with side sum 12. I'll try that first.

So how do three numbers add up to 12? Can I work that out systematically? Suppose I start with 1. What other two numbers add to 11? Just 5 and 6. So $1+5+6$ is one possibility.

Now start with 2. How do I get 10? I know $2+8=10$ but that's no good for two reasons. First, it would mean using a number above 6 and second, it would mean using 2 twice. So it looks as if the only way to get 12 is $2+4+6$. ($2+5+5$ needs 5 twice!)

Ah! If things keep going this easily I'll be done in no time. What are the other sums to 12? If I start with 3, I don't need to use any numbers smaller than 3 because I would have got them already starting with 1 or 2. So $(3+4+5=12)$!

Starting with 4 … . I can't. The smallest sum starting with 4 and not repeating 1, 2, 3 or 4 is $4+5+6=15$. Too big!

So I've only got to wangle $1+5+6$, $2+4+6$ and $3+4+5$ into my little circles! But that's easy. The number 6 is in exactly two sums, as is 4 and 5. That means there is only one way to get a mathmark with side sum 12 (omitting rotations and reflections). It was the one I got in Figure 3(b).

And surely that's the end of it. We...ell no! It seems to me that we've not used anything very sophisticated on this problem so far. How about stepping up to algebra at least?

In Figure 5, I've labelled the circles a through f. I certainly know that $\{a, b, c, d, e, f\} = \{1, 2, 3, 4, 5, 6\}$, so $a + b + c + d + e + f = 21$.

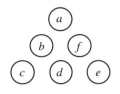

But there is an equation involving the side sums too.

$$(a + b + c) + (c + d + e) + (e + f + a) = 3X, \text{ where } X \text{ is the side sum.}$$

So
$$\begin{aligned} 3X &= (a + b + c) + (c + d + e) + (e + f + a) \\ &= (a + b + c + d + e + f) + (a + c + e) \\ &= 21 + (a + c + e). \end{aligned}$$

So the sum of the corners is $3X - 21$.

Exercises

5. What are all possible sums of the corners?
6. Find all the mathmarks with a side sum of 10.
7. The Emperor's children all have another mark, called an Empmark, tatooed on their foreheads. It consists of 9 squares arranged in the shape shown.
   These Empmarks have the numbers 1 through 9, one to a square, so that three consecutive horizontal and vertical bits add up to the same number.
   The key to finding a solution is to find the values of the "elbow" squares, c, e, and g.

   (i) To help you get started, I'll tell you that a possible value of $c + e + g$ is 7. What is the corresponding sum of each of the horizontal and vertical bits?
   (ii) Find one or two Empmarks using $c + e + g = 7$.
   (iii) What are the possible values of $c + e + g$?
   (iv) Find another Empmark using $c + e + g = 11$.

1.2   Problem Solving

What I was doing in the last section was problem solving. I had a problem that I had never seen before, that I had no idea how to solve, and I played around until I had solved the thing completely. Now the steps that I took to solve this problem were pretty much the steps that I'd take with **any** problem, whether it be a recreational puzzle (even a cryptic crossword puzzle) or a serious(!) mathematical research problem. What are these steps? In a nutshell, they are

1. Read the problem.
2. Choose a strategy.
3. Use a strategy.
4. Then look back.

1. Read the Problem

Reading the problem is so important that you should do it at least twice and probably more times. Certainly read it at the start to get going but definitely read it at the end to make sure that you have answered the problem that was given and not some other problem you invented along the way.

Key points

Watch out for the key pieces of information in a problem. Highlight them if you like. What are the key pieces? Maybe it's easier to say what are not. For instance, more than half the rubbish at the start of the last section was totally irrelevant. Strike out the planet Thrae, the Emperor, the Math Police (if you dare), and so on. The only use for mathmarks was a neat way to describe those circles in a triangular form.

As it turned out the key points were
* six circles;
* arranged as described in equilateral triangle;
* the numbers 1 to 6, one to a circle;
* the side sums being constant.

Once you've taken that out of the problem you'd be ready to start the solution. But you don't always know that. If you get stuck halfway along, then it's a good idea to reread the problem to see if you are missing a vital piece of information.

Panic

I invariably panic about now. How in the world am I going to be able to get this? I panic even more if someone is standing next to me and saying that it's an easy problem and I should have gotten it by now.

One of the important strategies in a problem solver's armour is **confidence**. All of the problems in this book are do-able. You should be able to do most of them. You may not necessarily be able to do them first time but you can do most of them after a little thought. If you're still stuck after a couple of weeks, don't look at the solution! Instead, ask a friend, a parent or a teacher. Even if nobody you know can do any math, talk to them anyway. Just talking often generates ideas.

2.   *Choose a strategy*

Here you want to find some of those ideas that I tried with the mathmarks, as well as others. I've listed a few below:

- draw a diagram;
- guess and check;
- make a table;
- make a list;
- try a simpler case;
- try a special case;
- work backwards;
- try algebra;
- look for a pattern.

All of these will be useful ideas for the problems in this book.

And don't be afraid to doodle. Guess a few things. Yes, **guess!** That's how I got started with the mathmarks. If you make a good guess, it'll probably lead on to a useful strategy and then a solution. No matter what you thought mathematics was about, you may not have realised that it involved a lot of guessing! But the guessing is based upon intuition, feel, and a lot of inspired doodling or experimenting.

3.   *Use a strategy*

There are lots of ways to use strategies but they all involve some math that you've been taught at some point. In the mathmarks we used a lot of number knowledge as well as some algebra and a certain amount of logical thinking.

This book contains problems, most of them shorter than mathmarks, on a range of subjects. You'll have to dig into your knowledge of analytic geometry, sequences and series, algebra, exponents and logarithms, trigonometry, calculus, counting and lots of other things beside. Sometimes, if you get stuck, it may be because you are missing a piece of mathematical knowledge. In that case you'll need to ask a teacher or look up a book on the topic.

4.   *Then look back*

As part of your looking back you'll need to think about your solution - to check it to see if all the steps are there. To do this, it's absolutely essential that you write out your solution. Until you've done this there is no way that you can be sure that you've got the complete solution.

As I said earlier, an important part of looking back is to read the question again. You may have overlooked some vital point.

In looking back you may also see a nicer way to do the problem. At this stage you should always try to find another solution. There are several reasons for this. First, if you can find another solution it provides confirmation that your first solution was correct. Second, one of these solutions may get straight to the heart of the problem and show you why the problem goes the way it does. And third, you may have discovered a method that you can use on lots of other problems.

Then there are extensions and generalisations. An **extension** is a problem a little like the one you've just solved but not exactly like it. A **generalisation** is a problem which contains the problem you have just solved as a special case. These two ideas are essential spurs to the development of mathematics.

An example of an extension of the mathmarks problem is to take the configuration of circles shown in Figure 6. Fill the circles with the number 4 to 9 so that the side sums are all the same.

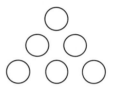

Figure 6

If you want a generalisation of the mathmarks problem, you can take any six consecutive numbers and ask in how many ways can you put them into the circles of Figure 1 so that the side sums are equal.

Sometimes extensions and generalisations can produce some very interesting problems.

Problems

If you get stuck on a problem, there are some hints beginning on page 113.

1.   Given as many 3¢ and 5¢ stamps as you like, what amounts of postage can you make?

2.   You are given that $1089 \times 9 = 9801$. Are there any other numbers whose digits are reversed on multiplying by 9?

3.   Here are two subtraction questions:

         400   4ab
         ab4   400
     The answers to the two subtractions are the same? What are *a* and *b*?

4. Circles with centres A, B, C have radii a, b, c respectively. Find c in terms of a and b.

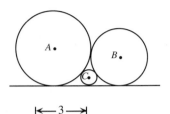

5. Show how to divide the shape shown into four identical, smaller shapes.

6. Delete a pair of opposite corners from a standard 8×8 chess board. Can the deleted chess board be covered with dominoes (2×1 rectangles)?

Chapter 2   *Analytic Geometry*

2.1   *Squares?*

I've always wondered how to make a square. Well, of course, I know how to make a square if I've got a ruler, compasses and a pencil. But what I'd like to be able to do is to **graph** a square. Everyone knows how to make straight lines and circles and things, but how about a square?

For instance, straight lines are things like $y = mx + c$, where m is the gradient or slope of the line and c is the y-intercept, the value of y where the graph crosses the y-axis. On the other hand, two points define a unique straight line. So if I'm given the two points $A(x_1, y_1)$ and $B(x_2, y_2)$, the line through A and B is $\dfrac{y - y_1}{y_2 - y_1} = \dfrac{x - x_1}{x_2 - x_1}$. Naturally, you can also define a line uniquely by its slope m and a point on the line.

In that case, you get the equation $y - y_1 = m(x - x_1)$. So I can get the equation of any old straight line by using one of these equations.

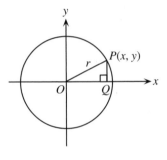

The easiest circles, equation-wise, are the ones whose centres are at the origin, O. In Figure 1, I've shown the circle with centre O and radius r. To get the equation of this circle we just have to use Pythagoras' Theorem on the right-angled triangle OPQ. Now

$$OQ^2 + QP^2 = OP^2,$$

Figure 1

so $x^2 + y^2 = r^2$ is the equation of the circle.

Similarly if the circle has centre $C(a, b)$ and radius r, we can use Pythagoras again to get its equation, which is $(x - a)^2 + (y - b)^2 = r^2$.

Exercises
1.   There's a little trouble with my equation of a line through A and B. What is the equation of the line through $A(5, 6)$ and $B(16, 6)$? What is the equation of the line through $C(5, 6)$ and $D(5, -3)$?

2.   I told you how to find the equation of a circle with centre $C(a, b)$ and radius r. But what if I know only some points on the circle? Can I find its equation then? And how many points do I need to be able to specify the circle? Will one point do? Two? Three? Four? More?

3.   Show that the equation of the circle with centre (a, b) and radius r is
$$(x - a)^2 + (y - b)^2 = r^2.$$

Let's see if I can find the equation of the circle through the
origin O and the point $A(6, 0)$. At this stage I only know how
to find the equation of a circle if I know its centre and radius.
Can I find the centre and radius working from the two points
O and A?

Looking at Figure 2, the centre of the circle through O and
A has to be on the perpendicular bisector of the line OA.
(This is shown dotted in Figure 2.) But **any** point on this
perpendicular bisector could be the centre of a circle
through O and A! So specifying **two** points is not enough
to define a circle precisely.

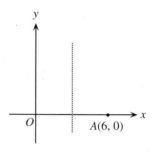

Figure 2

Let's add another point, say $B(3, 9)$.
The centre of any circle through O and B must be on the
perpendicular bisector of the line segment OB. Where the
two bisecting (dotted) lines meet, must be the centre C
(see Figure 3). If I could find the coordinates of C, I
could then use the fact that OC is a radius and then I'd be
able to write down the equation of the circle.

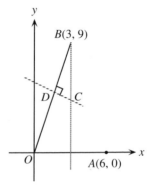

Figure 3

Exercises

4.   Find the equation of the circle through O, A and B in Figure 3.
5.   Find the equation of the circle through $A(1, -3)$, $B(6, 2)$ and $C(4, 6)$.
6.   Find the equation of the circle through $A(4, 2)$ and $B(-2, 2)$, given that AB is a diameter
     of the circle.

Of course, there are times when the equation of a circle isn't given neatly like
$(x - a)^2 + (y - b)^2 = r^2$. You might be given it in a form something like
$$x^2 + 4x + y^2 - 2y - 11 = 0.$$
To be able to recognize its centre and radius we'll have to do some tidying up. This is done by
completing some squares.

Now $x^2 + 4x = (x + 2)^2 - 4$ and $y^2 - 2y = (y - 1)^2 - 1$.

Hence the equation becomes
$$\left[(x + 2)^2 - 4\right] + \left[(y - 1)^2 - 1\right] - 11 = 0.$$

Tidying this up, I get

$$(x+2)^2 + (y-1)^2 - 16 = 0.$$

Hence $(x+2)^2 + (y-1)^2 = 16$ is the equation of the circle.

This circle has centre $(-2,1)$ and radius 4.

Exercises

7.   Find the centre and radius of the circles

   (a) $x^2 + 6x + y^2 - 4y - 12 = 0$.

   (b) $x^2 - 8x + y^2 + 4y = 5$.

8.   Find the diametrically opposite point on the circle $x^2 + y^2 - 10x + 8y + 16 = 0$ to the point $A(1, -1)$.

So I can find the equation of any circle once I know it's centre and radius. But how can I find the equation of a square? Does the square in Figure 4 actually have a nice equation or not? Maybe it doesn't.

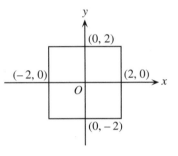

Figure 4

2.2   *The Absolute Value Function*

One of the new ideas that you may not have seen before is $|x|$. We call this the **absolute value** of x and define it by

$$|x| = \begin{cases} x, & \text{if } x \geq 0 \\ -x, & \text{if } x < 0. \end{cases}$$

This means that $|5| = 5$, $|-4| = -(-4) = 4$, $|\pi| = \pi$, $|-325.76| = 325.76$. Despite the sign in the definition, $|x|$ is **never negative**. If you like, you can think of it as a distance of x from the origin. We show this in Figure 5.

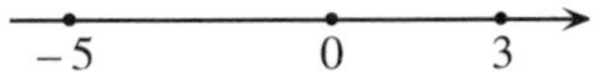

Figure 5

It should be clear, then, that if $|x| = 6$, then x can be either 6 or -6. Either of the points on the real line with $x = 6$ or $x = -6$ will be 6 units from the origin.

Once you've come this far, you can solve a whole host of equations. Look at $|2x + 3| = 7$, for instance. Suppose we let $z = 2x + 3$. Then we're looking first of all for z such that $|z| = 7$. Hence $z = \pm 7$. And now we can go back to x because we know that either $2x + 3 = 7$ or $2x + 3 = -7$. A little bit of algebra will finish this off and show you that $x = 2$ or -5.

Exercises

9.   Solve the following equations:

      (i) $|x + 1| = 8$;   (ii) $|3x - 7| = 5$;

      (iii) $|7 - 3x| = 5$;   (iv) $|x^2 - 8| = 1$;

      (v) $|x + 1| = |x|$;   (vi) $|2x - 3| = |3x + 2|$.

10.   Solve the following inequalities:

      (i) $|x - 1| > 8$;   (ii) $|3x + 7| \le 5$.

But some of this absolute value stuff is more easily done using graphs. So what is the graph of $y = |x|$? Go back to basics if you can't see it straight away.

$$y = |x| = \begin{cases} x, & \text{if } x \ge 0 \\ -x, & \text{if } x < 0. \end{cases}$$

What does that tell us? Where is $x \ge 0$? Wherever it is, $y = x$ there. Where is $x < 0$? Wherever it is, $y = -x$ there. Now we know what the graph of $y = x$ and $y = -x$ look like. They're just straight lines through the origin, one with slope 1 the other with slope -1. That's interesting; they're actually perpendicular lines because the product of their slopes is -1. So, if we only knew where $x \ge 0$ was we could put $y = x$ there. If we knew where $x < 0$, then we could put $y = -x$.

But the region in the plane where $x \ge 0$ is everything from the y-axis to the right - essentially the first and fourth quadrants. In this region, $y = x$. So $y = |x|$ looks like $y = x$ to the right of the y-axis.

On the other hand, $x < 0$ is to the left of the y-axis. So $y = |x|$ is $y = -x$ to the left of the y-axis. Putting these two parts of the graph together, we get the graph in Figure 6.

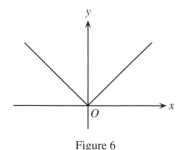

Figure 6

Once you've got this far you can go anywhere with graphs involving the absolute value function. All you have to remember to do is to split things up into the parts where things are positive or zero and where things are negative.

Take a look at $y = \left| x^2 - 9 \right|$. What's its graph? Well

$$y = \left| x^2 - 9 \right| = \begin{cases} x^2 - 9, & \text{if } x^2 - 9 \geq 0 \\ -\left(x^2 - 9\right), & \text{if } x^2 - 9 < 0. \end{cases}$$

You should be able to graph $y = x^2 - 9$ and $y = -\left(x^2 - 9\right)$. These are just parabolas. The problem might be to sort out the region where $x^2 - 9 \geq 0$ and the region where $x^2 - 9 < 0$.

If $x^2 - 9 \geq 0$, then $x^2 \geq 9$. Hence $x \geq 3$ or $x \leq -3$. I've shown that region (shaded in Figure 7.)

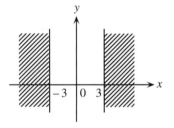

Figure 7

What about $x^2 - 9 < 0$? Here $x^2 < 9$, so $-3 < x < 3$. That's just the unshaded region in Figure 7.

So to draw the graph of $y = \left| x^2 - 9 \right|$, we have to put the graph of $y = x^2 - 9$ in this shaded region and the graph of $y = -\left(x^2 - 9\right)$ in the unshaded region. This I've done in Figure 8.

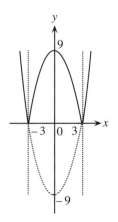

Figure 8

Notice that we can get the graph of $y=\left|x^2-9\right|$ by first drawing the graph of $y=x^2-9$ and then just taking the part of the parabola that is below the x-axis and reflect it in the x-axis.

Exercises

11. Sketch the graphs of the following functions:

     (i) $y=\left|2x\right|$;   (ii) $y=\left|2x-3\right|$;   (iii) $y=\left|3-2x\right|$;

     (iv) $y=\left|x^2-1\right|$;   (v) $y=3-\left|x\right|$.

12. Shade the following regions of the plane:

     (i) $y\le\left|x-2\right|$;   (ii) $y\ge\left|x^2-4\right|$.

2.3   *Squares!*

Sketch the graph of $\left|y\right|+\left|x\right|=1$.

To do this, we split the plane up into four regions.

(i) $x\ge0,\ y\ge0$ gives us $y+x=1$ or $y=-x+1$;

(ii) $x\ge0,\ y<0$ gives us $-y+x=1$ or $y=x-1$;

(iii) $x<0,\ y\ge0$ gives us $y-x=1$ or $y=x+1$;

(iv) $x<0,\ y<0$ gives us $-y-x=1$ or $y=-x-1$.

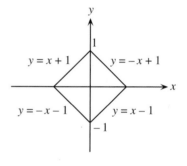

Figure 9

Putting these together we get their graph in Figure 9. Well, it's a diamond! Actually, it's a square that's tilted $45°$.

Can we get a square with its sides parallel to the axes?

Exercise

13. Sketch the graph of $\left|y-x\right|+\left|y+x\right|=2$.

2.4   *Essential Skills*

In this chapter, there are a number of mathematical skills that you will need in order to be able to do the problems. Check through the list that I've written out below and make sure that you are comfortable with everything. Then read through the next two sections before going on to the problems.

It's worth noting at this point that you may be able to do the problems without using some of the items on my list. That's fine. However, if you are stuck on a problem it's a good idea to come back and look at the list. You may see something there that's useful for you.

Pythagoras' Theorem

In the right-angled triangle ABC (see the diagram), the square on the hypotenuse is equal to the sum of the squares on the other two sides.

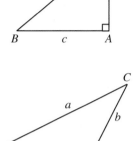

$$AB^2 + AC^2 = BC^2$$

$$b^2 + c^2 = a^2$$

The Cosine Rule

In any triangle ABC, the square on the side opposite angle A is equal to the sum of the squares on the other two sides minus twice the product of the other sides times the cosine of angle A.

$$a^2 = b^2 + c^2 - 2bc\ \cos A$$

[Note that the cosine rule is a generalisation of Pythagoras' Theorem because when $A = 90°$, $\cos A = 0$ and we get $a^2 = b^2 + c^2$].

The Equations of a Line

With slope m and y-intercept c:　$y = mx + c$.

With slope m and through (x_1, y_1):　$y - y_1 = m(x - x_1)$.

Through the two points (x_1, y_1), (x_2, y_2):　$\dfrac{y - y_1}{y_2 - y_1} = \dfrac{x - x_1}{x_2 - x_1}$.

The Equation of a Circle

With centre (a, b) and radius r:　$(x - a)^2 + (y - b)^2 = r^2$.

The Equations of other Conics

Parabola:　$y = ax^2 + bx + c$.

Ellipse with centre (x_1, y_1) and semi-axes a and b:　$\dfrac{(x - x_1)^2}{a^2} + \dfrac{(y - y_1)^2}{b^2} = 1$.

Solutions of Equations

Quadratic:　If $ax^2 + bx + c = 0$, then $x = \dfrac{-b \pm \sqrt{b^2 - 4ac}}{2a}$.

Roots of a quadratic equation:　If $ax^2 + bx + c = 0$, has roots r and s, then $rs = \dfrac{c}{a}$ and $r + s = \dfrac{-b}{a}$.

Simultaneous linear equations:　$ax + by = c$

$dx + ey = f$.

One way to solve the equation is to multiply the first equation by d and the second by a and subtract to give y; substitute in either equation for y to give x.

[Note that these equations will have a unique solution if the lines they represent have different slopes. If the lines are parallel, then $\dfrac{-a}{b} = \dfrac{-d}{e}$, and there is no point of intersection. If the lines are the same, then there are an infinite number of points of intersection].

Simultaneous linear and quadratic equations: $ax + by = c$
$$dx^2 + ex + fy^2 + gy + h = 0$$
Solve the linear equation for y or x and substitute in the quadratic equation.

Other Basic Facts

- If a tangent and the radius of a circle meet at a point, they are perpendicular.
- The area of a trapezoid (trapezium) is the product of the average of the two parallel sides times the perpendicular height.

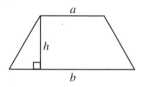

$$area = \frac{1}{2}(a+b)h$$

- If two lines with slopes m, and m_2 are perpendicular, then $m_1 m_2 = -1$.
- The coordinates of the midpoint of the line segment AB, where $A = (x_1, y_1)$ and

$B = (x_2, y_2)$, is given by $\left(\dfrac{x_1 + x_2}{2}, \dfrac{y_1 + y_2}{2} \right)$.

2.5   *Problem Solving Skills*

For this chapter, of course, all the problem solving skills that I mentioned in Chapter 1 may be applicable. There are, however, a number of skills that are especially important for this chapter, so let's consider them now.

Diagram

In any geometry problem it's almost mandatory to draw a diagram. Sometimes we have generously given you a drawing to start with. Almost always when we haven't, the first thing you should do is to draw one.

There are a couple of important points about drawing diagrams. First, make them large so that you can easily put crucial points, construction lines and the like onto the diagram without cluttering them up. Second, make them as general as the problem requires. So if the problem is something about a triangle, don't draw an equilateral triangle or an isosceles triangle unless you are specifically told what type of triangle it is. Assuming properties of the triangle will almost always lead you astray.

Beware

If you draw your diagram carefully to scale, do not expect to be able to get an answer from your diagram by direct measurement. It is unlikely that you will be able either to construct or to measure sufficiently accurately to get the required answers. For instance, if the answer is $\sqrt{21}$, your instruments will certainly not be sufficiently accurate. You may be able to use measurement to check that the answer you have found is in the right ball park but you can never be sure of the accuracy of an answer obtained by measuring.

Analytic

This chapter is about **analytic** geometry. That invariably means that you will need to combine algebra with the geometry. After you have drawn your diagrams you will almost always have to set up some equation or equations which will then need to be solved. If you're lucky, solving these equations will provide the solution to the problem. Many of the problems we have posed just require the steps:

Step 1:   draw a diagram

Step 2:   set up some equations

Step 3:   solve the equations

Step 4:   solve the problem.

The key step in the problem is very often the finding of the right equation(s). We'll leave you to sort out the other problems for yourself.

Problems

If you get stuck on a problem, there are some hints beginning on page 113.

1.   For the circle with centre $(3, 4)$ and radius 2, find the length of the tangent from the origin to the circle.

2.   In the diagram, each rectangle has the same area. Determine this area.

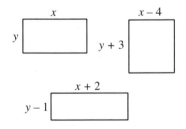

3.   A quadrilateral in the first quadrant is bounded by lines $x = 0$, $y = 0$, $x = 3$, and $y = mx + 4$. If the area of the quadrilateral is 9, determine the value of m.

4.   Determine the equation, $y = f(x)$, of a straight line, given $f(3) = 7$ and $f(-3) = -5$.

5.   (a)   On the same set of axes, sketch the graphs of $y = x$ and $y = |3x - 8|$.

     (b)   Determine all values of x such that $x > |3x - 8|$.

6.   Find the sum of all values of x for which $|x + 3| = 2|x - 3|$.

7.   Find all values of k so that the circle with equation $x^2 + y^2 = k^2$ will intersect the circle with equation $(x - 5)^2 + (y + 12)^2 = 49$ in exactly one point.

8.   On the circle $x^2 + y^2 = 1$, find the coordinates of the point which is nearest to $(-4, 3)$.

9.   A circle whose equation is $x^2 + y^2 = 5$ and a parabola whose equation is $y^2 = 4x$ intersect in two points, A and B.

     (a)   Sketch the graph of the circle and parabola.

     (b)   Find the length of AB.

10.   (a)   The line with equation $5x - y - 13 = 0$ intersects the circle whose equation is $x^2 + y^2 = 13$ at points A and B. Determine the coordinates of the midpoint of chord AB.

     (b)   Repeat part (a) using the line $y = 2x - 3$.

11.   The point A is on the x-axis and the point B is on the line $2x + y = 0$. If $(2, 1)$ is the midpoint of AB, determine the coordinates of point A.

12.   The line with equation $y = x - 2$ intersects the circle with equation $(x - 2)^2 + (y - 1)^2 = 25$ at the points A and B, with B in the first quadrant. At B a line is drawn perpendicular to the given line to meet the circle again at point C. Determine the area of $\triangle ABC$.

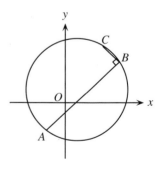

13. The circle with equation $(x-3)^2 + y^2 = 25$ passes
    through the point $A(7,3)$ and intersects the y-axis at
    points B and C, as shown.
    (a) Determine the coordinates of B and C.
    (b) Determine the measure of $\angle BAC$.

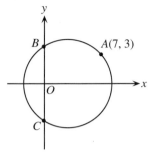

14. For the curve with equation $y = \dfrac{2x^2 - x - 1}{x^2 - 2x - 3}$, determine:
    (a) all x- and y-intercepts
    (b) all vertical asymptotes
    (c) the horizontal asymptote
    (d) the number of points of intersection of the curve and the horizontal asymptote

15. A tangent is drawn from $O(0,0)$ to the circle defined by the equation
    $(x-5)^2 + (y-7)^2 = 25$. What is the distance from the origin to the point of contact of
    the tangent?

16. The point Q is a local maximum point, and points P
    and R are local minimum points for the graph of the
    fourth degree polynomial $y = f(x)$, as shown in the
    diagram. What are the values of k for which the
    equation $f(x) + k = 0$ has four different real roots?

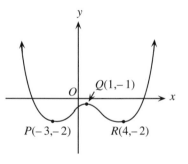

17. Sketch the graph of $|y - x| + |x| = 2$.

Chapter 3   Sequences and Series

3.1   Some History

There are two mathematical stories that I know about schoolboys but I can't for the life of me think of one relating to schoolgirls, unless its Kirkman's schoolgirl problem. I'm inclined to think that this bias towards males in mathematics is an historical accident. In the 21st Century I fully expect some balance to come in. The signs are there. It's just a matter of time.

So what are the schoolboy stories? The first one goes back to Carl Friedrick Gauss. One day, in class, he was given the task of adding all the numbers from 1 to 100 inclusive. For many years, his teacher had been using that as a device to keep his students busy. He knew that it always took them quite a while. Imagine his surprise when young Carl came up with the correct answer in a matter of seconds!

Exercises
1. How did Carl do it?
2. Find out something about Gauss. Where did he go to school? Where did he work? What contributions did he make to mathematics?
3. Who was Kirkman? What was his schoolgirl problem?

The other mathematical schoolboy was young Fred Guthrie. He was doing his geography homework one night when he decided to colour in the counties of England. With a bit of experimentation, he found that he could colour England so that neighbouring counties had different colours, and he could do it with at most four colours.

Fred told his brother Francis, who was a student of de Morgan's at London University, and Francis told de Morgan. And this launched the famous Four Colour Theorem on its way. The idea that Fred had was that, no matter how you divided up the surface of the Earth, into counties, or countries, you never needed more than four colours. This, of course, was subject to the restriction that no two countries with a common border could be coloured in the same colour.

It took over a hundred years before the Four Colour Theorem was finally proved. In the end, it required the full might of the computer to clinch the proof. As a result the proof sparked a controversy, a rare thing in mathematical circles. It was the first major mathematical result that relied upon a computer. Some mathematicians felt that if you couldn't check it, it wasn't a proof, and it was certainly impossible, by hand, to check everything that the computer had done.

Exercises
4. Who proved the Four Colour Theorem and when?
5. It's possible I've missed a third schoolboy story. Have you ever felt like throwing something at an examiner? A young French mathematician did. He was also involved in a duel. Who was he? Why did he throw the duster at his examiner? What contribution did he make to mathematics? How did the duel go?

Perhaps we should get back to Gauss. His little trick was to go forwards and backwards. Suppose S is the sum of the numbers from 1 to 100 inclusive, then

$$S = 1 + 2 + 3 + 4 + ... + 97 + 98 + 99 + 100,$$

and $S = 100 + 99 + 98 + 97 + ... + 4 + 3 + 2 + 1.$

If we add these two equations together carefully we notice something interesting.

$$2S = (1 + 100) + (2 + 99) + (3 + 98) + ... + (98 + 3) + (99 + 2) + (100 + 1).$$

What's interesting is that each of the pairs of numbers in brackets adds up to 101. Since there are 100 pairs, $2S = 100 \times 101$

$$S = 101 \times 50$$
$$= 5050.$$

And that was Gauss' trick.

Exercises
6.   Add up the first 200 natural numbers.
7.   What's the sum of all the integers between 1001 and 2000?
8.   (a)   What's the sum of all the even integers from 2 to 150?
         (b)   What's the sum of all the integers between 13 and 94 which are divisible by 3?

One of the good things about Gauss' trick is that it works in a large number of cases. All you need is a set of numbers where there is the same difference between consecutive terms. I'm talking about sets like

$$a, a + d, a + 2d, ..., a + (n - 2)d, a + (n - 1)d,$$

where the first term is a and the common difference between consecutive terms is d. Such a set of numbers is called an **Arithmetic Sequence** or **Arithmetic Progression** (abbreviated A.P.)

The A.P. above has n terms and we'll show how Gauss can work his magic on it.

$$S = a + (a + d) + (a + 2d) + ... + [a + (n - 3)d] + [a + (n - 2)d] + [a + (n - 1)d]$$

Adding the terms in reverse order gives

$$S = [a + (n - 1)d] + [a + (n - 2)d] + [a + (n - 3)d] + ... + (a + 2d) + (a + d) + a.$$

$$2S = [a + a + (n - 1)d] + [(a + d) + a + (n - 2)d] + ... + [a + (n - 1)d + a]$$
$$= [2a + (n - 1)d] + [2a + (n - 1)d] + ... + [2a + (n - 1)d]$$
$$= n[2a + (n - 1)d]$$

Hence $S = \frac{1}{2}n[2a + (n - 1)d]$.

Exercises

9. If the A.P. contains only integers, S has to be an integer too. Surely though, because we're dividing by 2, there must be some occasions when S is a fraction. Is there something wrong here?

10. Is it possible for a and d not to be integers? Will the formula for the sum of terms of an A.P. still work in this case?

One other aspect of notation that's worth mentioning is that it would actually be more useful to us if we use S_n instead of S. That way we know the number of terms we are dealing with. So in the first A.P. we looked at, 1, 2, 3, ..., 100, $a = 1$, $d = 1$ and $S_{100} = 5050$.

I think you'll also find it useful to have notation available for the terms of an A.P.. So we use t_n for the nth term. This means that in the general A.P., a, $a+d$, $a+2d$, ..., $a+(n-1)d$, we'll write $t_1 = a$, $t_2 = a+d$, $t_3 = a+d$ and $t_n = a+(n-1)d$. Once we know a and d, then it's easy to write down the general, or nth term, as $t_n = a+(n-1)d$.

Exercises

11. (a) Find the 15th term in the A.P. of Exercise 7.

    (b) Find the 10th term in the A.P.s of Exercise 8.

Another important and common series is the **Geometric Sequence** or **Geometric Progression** (abbreviated G.P.). Here we **multiply** successive terms by a common quantity, rather than adding as we did with the Arithmetic Progression. If a is the first term of a G.P., then all n terms of a G.P. are

$$a, ar, ar^2, ..., ar^{n-1}$$

where r is the common ratio.

A typical example of a G.P. is 2, 6, 18, 54, ..., where $a = 2$ and $r = 3$. Notice that $t_1 = 2 \times 3^0 = 2$, $t_2 = 2 \times 3^1 = 6$, $t_3 = 2 \times 3^2 = 18, ..., t_n = 2 \times 3^{n-1}$.

The obvious question then is, what is the sum of the first n terms of a G.P.? Gauss' method doesn't quite work here but something very close does.

If $S_n = a + ar + ar^2 + ... + ar^{n-1}$,

then $rS_n = ar + ar^2 + ar^3 + ... + ar^{n-1} + ar^n$.

Instead of adding, we now subtract. The reason for this is the fact that S_n and rS_n have a lot of terms in common. So let's subtract.

$$S_n - rS_n = a - ar^n.$$

Hence $(1-r)S_n = a(1-r^n)$.

This gives $S_n = \dfrac{a(1-r^n)}{1-r}$.

Exercises

12.   Is S_n in the last formula valid for **all** values of r? Does r have to be less than one?

13.   (a)   Find the sum of the first 10 terms of the G.P. 3, 6, 12, 24 ... .

(b)   What is the nth term of the G.P. $\dfrac{1}{2}, \dfrac{1}{4}, \dfrac{1}{8}, ...$?

14.   Is it possible for a series of numbers to be both an A.P. and a G.P.?

It's actually worth looking at the G.P. $\dfrac{1}{2}, \dfrac{1}{4}, \dfrac{1}{8}$, ... again.

Now $S_n = \dfrac{\dfrac{1}{2}\left[1-\left(\dfrac{1}{2}\right)^n\right]}{1-\dfrac{1}{2}} = 1-\left(\dfrac{1}{2}\right)^n$. The interesting thing about this is that as n gets larger, $\left(\dfrac{1}{2}\right)^n$

gets smaller. So S_n approaches one. This can be written $\lim\limits_{n\to\infty} S_n = 1$.

But we get similar behaviour for ratios other than $\dfrac{1}{2}$. As long as $|r|<1$, $r^n \to 0$ as $n \to \infty$.

So if $|r|<1$, $\lim\limits_{n\to\infty} S_n = \lim\limits_{n\to\infty} \dfrac{a(1-r^n)}{1-r} = \dfrac{a}{1-r}$.

Thus the sum to infinity of a G.P. with $|r|<1$, is $\dfrac{a}{1-r}$. We usually denote the sum to infinity

by S. So, for $|r|<1$, $S = \dfrac{a}{1-r}$.

3.2   Essential Skills

Below we list the mathematical skills that may be called into play to solve the problems of this chapter. Naturally, there may well be things in the first two chapters that might come in handy too. So if you are looking for inspiration, you should comb through the list below first. If that doesn't work try the advice given earlier.

Arithmetic Progression

An A.P. is a sequence of numbers of the form a, $a+d$, $a+2d$, ..., $a+(n-1)d$, ... The nth term of an A.P. is $t_n = a+(n-1)d$.

The sum of n terms of an A.P. is found by the average of the first and last terms multiplied by the number of terms.

This gives $S_n = \dfrac{(t_1 + t_n)}{2} n$.

If we let $t_n = t_1 + (n-1)d$, we get the other formula for S_n, namely $S_n = \dfrac{n}{2}[2t_1 + (n-1)d]$.

Geometric Progression

A G.P. is a sequence of numbers of the form $a,\ ar,\ ar^2,\ ...,\ ar^{n-1},\ ...\ .$

The nth term of a G.P. is $t_n = ar^{n-1}$.

The sum of n terms of a G.P. is given by the formula $S_n = \dfrac{a(1 - r^n)}{1 - r}$, where $r \ne 1$.

The sum to infinity of a G.P. with $|r| < 1$ is given by

$$S = \dfrac{a}{1 - r}.$$

Mathematical Induction

This is a method of proof which enables statements to be proved for all natural numbers n. Hence it is ideal for entities like A.P.'s and G.P.'s. The proof proceeds in three steps.

Step 1:   Show the statement is true for some small value of n. (Usually $n = 1$).

Step 2:   Assume that the statement is true for $n = k$.

Step 3:   Show that the statement is true for $n = k + 1$, making use of the assumption of Step 2.

Prime Numbers

A prime number is a natural number other than one, which is only divisible by itself and one. The only even prime number is 2.

Angles in a Polygon

The sum of the exterior angles of a polygon is $360°$. The sum of the interior angles of a polygon with n sides is $180°(n - 2)$.

3.3   Problem Solving Skills

In this section we highlight the problem solving skills that are likely to be required in this chapter. Naturally it is worth being aware of the full range of problem solving skills that we discussed in Chapter 1.

Looking for Patterns

This is a key problem solving skill in this chapter as you will sometimes have to decide what kind of sequence is being used, and so which formulas are required.

Be flexible and be ready to use the basic Essential Skills in novel ways.

3.4 *Some Other Series*

We've seen how to find the sum of n of the numbers 1, 2, 3, ... We know that the sum of the first n natural numbers is $1 + 2 + 3 + ... + n = \frac{1}{2}n(n+1)$.

But there are other similar sums that are of interest. For instance, is there a nice formula for $S = 1^2 + 2^2 + ... + n^2$? Of course, there is, and we can establish the formula in at least two ways. First of all, we tackle this sum using the difference of various cubes.

$$n^3 - (n-1)^3 = 3n^2 - 3n + 1 \qquad \text{(You should check this.)}$$
$$(n-1)^3 - (n-2)^3 = 3(n-1)^2 - 3(n-1) + 1$$
$$(n-2)^3 - (n-3)^3 = 3(n-2)^2 - 3(n-2) + 1$$

...   .

$$3^3 - 2^3 = 3.3^2 - 3.3 + 1$$
$$2^3 - 1^3 = 3.2^2 - 3.2 + 1$$
$$1^3 - 0^3 = 3.1^2 - 3.1 + 1.$$

Adding up all the terms on the left hand sides of these equations gives just n^3. Everything else cancels out. Things on the right hand side are a little more interesting though. There we get

$$\left[3.1^2 + 3.2^2 + ... + 3.(n+1)^2 + 3n^2\right] - \left[3.1 + 3.2 + ... + 3(n-1) + 3n\right] + \left[1 + 1 + ... + 1\right].$$

This breaks down into three pieces. Going backwards, $[1 + 1 + ... + 1] = n$ because there are n ones.

$$[3.1 + 3.2 + ... + 3.n] = 3(1 + 2 + ... + n) = \frac{3n}{2}(n+1).$$

Finally $\left[3.1^2 + 3.2^2 + ... + 3n^2\right] = 3\left(1^2 + 2^2 + ... + n^2\right)$ and this is three times S and S is what we're looking for.

So putting all that together we get

$$n^3 = 3S - \frac{3n}{2}(n+1) + n.$$

Hence $3S = n^3 + \frac{3n}{2}(n+1) - n$

$$= \frac{1}{2}n\left[2n^2 + 3(n+1) - 2\right]$$
$$= \frac{1}{2}n\left[2n^2 + 3n + 1\right]$$
$$= \frac{1}{2}n(n+1)(2n+1).$$

So $S = \frac{1}{6}n(n+1)(2n+1)$.

This is a perfectly satisfactory proof. What if someone had given us this formula without the proof? That is, suppose that someone told us that they understood that the sum of the squares of consecutive integers 1, 2, 3, ..., n was $\frac{1}{6}n(n+1)(2n+1)$. Then we can justify this using mathematical induction.

Required to show $1^2 + 2^2 + 3^2 + ... + n^2 = \frac{1}{6}n(n+1)(2n+1)$.

Step 1:   The statement is true for $n = 1$. To show this, note that for $n = 1$, LHS $= 1$ and

RHS $= \frac{1}{6} \times 1 \times 2 \times 3 = 1$.

Step 2:   Assume the statement is true for $n = k$. Hence assume that

$1^2 + 2^2 + 3^2 + ... + k^2 = \frac{1}{6}k(k+1)(2k+1)$ is a true statement.

Step 3:   Prove the statement is true for $n = k+1$. We have to show that the original statement is true for $n = k+1$, and we must use our assumption in Step 2 to do it.

$$1^2 + 2^2 + 3^2 + ... + (k+1)^2 = \left[1^2 + 2^2 + 3^2 + ... + k^2\right] + (k+1)^2$$

$$= \frac{1}{6}k(k+1)(2k+1) + (k+1)^2 \quad \text{(There! We used our assumption.)}$$

$$= \frac{1}{6}(k+1)\left[k(2k+1) + 6(k+1)\right]$$

$$= \frac{1}{6}(k+1)\left[2k^2 + 7k + 6\right]$$

$$= \frac{1}{6}(k+1)(k+2)(2k+3)$$

$$= \frac{1}{6}(k+1)\big((k+1)+1\big)\big(2(k+1)+1\big).$$

This is just what the formula would give us for $n = k+1$.

So the formula is valid for $n = k+1$ whenever it is valid for $n = k$, and since it is valid for $n = 1$, by mathematical induction it is valid for all n.

Exercises

15.   Find a simple expression for $1^3 + 2^3 + 3^3 + ... + n^3$. As a suggestion, try a few sums to see if you can guess at the formula, then prove it by mathematical induction.

16.   Find a simple expression for the sum of the squares of the first n even integers.

Problems

If you get stuck on a problem, there are some hints beginning on page 113.

1. What is the number of terms in the arithmetic sequence $-1994, -1992, -1990, ..., 1992,$ 1994?

2. In the sequence $5, 3, -2, -5, ...$, each term after the first two is constructed by taking the preceding term and subtracting the term before it. What is the sum of the first 32 terms of the sequence?

3. Evaluate $\sin\left(\frac{\pi}{6}\right) + \sin^2\left(\frac{\pi}{6}\right) + \sin^3\left(\frac{\pi}{6}\right) + ...$.

4. How many terms in the arithmetic sequence $7, 14, 21, ...$ are between 40 and 28 001?

5. If f is a function such that $f(1) = 2$ and $f(n+1) = \dfrac{3f(n)+1}{3}$ for $n = 1, 2, 3, ...$, what is the value of $f(100)$?

6. The interior angles of a polygon, measured in degrees, form an arithmetic sequence. The smallest angle is $120°$ and the common difference is $5°$. Determine the number of sides in the polygon.

7. If the terms $27, x, y, 8$ form a geometric sequence, find x and y.

8. Determine the value of n for which $2^1 \cdot 2^2 \cdot 2^3 \cdot 2^4 \cdot ... \cdot 2^n = 2^{210}$.

9. The sum of 25 consecutive integers is 500. Determine the smallest of the 25 integers.

10. For the family of lines with equations of the form $px + qy = r$, and which all pass through the point $(-1, 2)$, prove that p, q, and r are consecutive terms of an arithmetic sequence.

11. The sum of the first n terms of a sequence is $S_n = 3^n - 1$, where n is a positive integer.
    (i)   If t_n represents the nth term of the sequence, determine t_1, t_2, t_3.
    (ii) Prove that $\dfrac{t_{n+1}}{t_n}$ is constant for all values of n.

12. If $(1 + 3 + 5 + ... + p) + (1 + 3 + 5 + ... + q) = (1 + 3 + 5 + ... + 19)$ where p and q are odd positive integers, evaluate $p + q$.

13. For n a positive integer, let $p = 1 + 3 + 3^2 + \cdots + 3^n$. Show that $1 + 9 + 9^2 + \cdots + 9^n$ is the sum of the integers from 1 to p.

14. As shown below, a figure consists of an infinite sequence of squares which have sides of length 1, s, s^2, s^3, ..., where $0 < s < 1$.

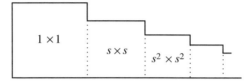

1×1

$s \times s$

$s^2 \times s^2$

   (a) Let A be the area of the figure. Express A in terms of s.
   (b) Let P be the outside perimeter of the figure. Express P in terms of s.
   (c) Determine all s such that $\frac{A}{P} = \frac{8}{35}$.

15. Prove, for all natural numbers n, that $1^2 + 3^2 + 5^2 + \cdots + (2n-1)^2 \geq n^3$.

16. The sums of n terms of two arithmetic series are in the ratio $(7n+1):(4n+27)$. Determine the ratio of their eleventh terms.

17. Divide 1 into four parts forming an arithmetic sequence such that the sum of their cubes is $\frac{1}{10}$.

Chapter 4   *Algebra*

4.1   *Painting Rooms*

Suppose Peter can paint a room in 2 hours on his own and Sue can paint the same room in 3 hours. How long will it take if they both work together?

You might like to take a few moments to try to solve that problem. I'll just hang around and wait. But don't you dare read on until you've at least struggled with it for a while.

Mathematical problems invariably involve a couple of steps. The first one is setting up the problem in a mathematical form and the second is using some mathematical skills to solve the mathematical form. (After you've done all that, of course, it's worth looking back to see that the mathematical solution makes sense. If you've found the height of a barn to be -3 metres or the distance between two cities to be 1.5 million kilometres, then you've more than likely made a mistake somewhere.)

We've already seen these two sides to solving problems. There have been a lot of examples in the last few chapters. Let's see if we can do it now with the painting problem that you've probably solved already. How did you do it? No, don't tell me. Did it go like this?

Peter and Sue will paint a different fraction of the room. Suppose Peter paints p and Sue paints s of the room; then $p + s = 1$. That's a nice equation but it's not much good to me at the moment. There are zillions of fractions p and s which add to 1 and very few of them have anything to do with painting this particular room. It would help if we could find some link between p and s. If we could get another equation then we'd be in business.

Exercises
1. Is there some relation between p and s? What is it?
2. How would things be changed if Sue could do the room in 4 hours, while Peter needed 5 hours?

The only piece of information that I can see that might be useful at all is the fact that Peter takes 2 hours and Sue takes 3 hours. Surely this will give us a link between the p and s somehow? But how?

Let's do a bit of guessing. Maybe p is just a multiple of s. If it is, this would be the simplest relation to exist between them. Better that than $p = \alpha s + \beta$ or $(p - a)2 + (s - b)2 = c2$ or something even worse. So let's hope this thing is simple.

Now if p is a multiple of s then $\frac{p}{s}$ is a constant. We know that there's a 2 and a 3 floating round in the questions, so maybe $\frac{p}{s} = \frac{3}{2}$, or possibly $\frac{p}{s} = \frac{2}{3}$.

Exercise

3.   Solve for p and s if $p + s = 1$ and

   (i) $\frac{p}{s} = \frac{3}{2}$ (ii) $\frac{p}{s} = \frac{2}{3}$.

Clearly only one of the equations involving $\frac{p}{s}$ can possibly be true. Let's just push our way through and see what we find.

First of all, if $\frac{p}{s} = \frac{3}{2}$, then $p + s = 1$ becomes $\frac{3}{2}s + s = 1$, so $s = \frac{2}{5}$. This immediately gives us $p = \frac{3}{5}$.

The second equation gives $\frac{p}{s} = \frac{2}{3}$, so $\frac{2}{3}s + s = 1$ and hence $\frac{5s}{3} = 1$, so in this case $s = \frac{3}{5}$ and $p = \frac{2}{5}$.

Well, which is it, $s = \frac{2}{5}$ or $s = \frac{3}{5}$? or is it neither? And if it is one, how can you justify the equation which gave the correct answer? I'll let you ponder on that for a minute or two.

Where we're currently at is a typical problem solving position. You can get part of the way and you kind of think that something might work. Then you get an answer and you need to be sure it's the right one. If it is, you need to justify the part that you guessed.

If Peter can paint the room in 2 hours while Sue takes 3 hours, he surely paints more quickly. It follows, then, that if they paint together he will paint a greater portion of the room. Hence the answer that makes sense is $p = \frac{3}{5}$ and $s = \frac{2}{5}$.

4.2   Solving Equations

Sometimes when we're solving a problem, we set things up as an equation (or equations) that must be solved. We saw that in the last section, where the equations were fairly easy to deal with. Unfortunately, it isn't always easy. So I want to spend a little while delving into some of the mysteries of equation solving.

We've already had a look at quadratic equations in Chapter 2 in the context of circles. For the moment let's forget the y's and concentrate solely on x's. How can we solve $ax^2 + bx + c = 0$?

You know that there is a formula which gives the two roots as

$$x = \frac{-b \pm \sqrt{b^2 - 4ac}}{2a}.$$

This will always work but sometimes it's a little easier to factorise the left hand side of the equation. This is most easily done when the roots are integers or fractions.

But maybe a quadratic doesn't have any real roots. We show the three possible situations for $y = ax^2 + bx + c$, where $a > 0$ in Figure 1. Here we concentrate on their behaviour with respect to the x-axis.

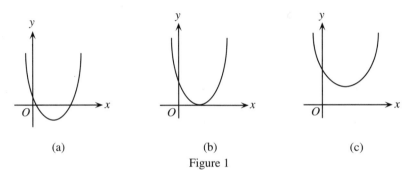

(a)   (b)   (c)

Figure 1

In Figure 1(a) the quadratic has two roots, in Figure 1(b) it has a unique root, and in Figure 1(c) there are no real roots at all. To see what's going on here, we indulge in the good problem-solving strategy of looking at an extreme case. First of all, then, what's going on in Figure 1(b)?

When I gave the general solution to the quadratic equation a minute or two ago, we had

$$x = \frac{-b \pm \sqrt{b^2 - 4ac}}{2a}.$$

In order for there to be only **one** solution the $\pm$ has to become inoperative. Essentially if it is ± 0, then there will only be one root $x = \frac{-b}{2a}$. To get this zero, we need $b^2 - 4ac = 0$. So the unique root case will arrive when $b^2 - 4ac = 0$.

The quantity $b^2 - 4ac$ is such a well used entity that it has its own name. It's called the **discriminant** of the quadratic. And now we're in business. If the discriminant is positive $\sqrt{b^2 - 4ac}$ will have a value and so there will be two roots for the quadratic. This is the case in Figure 1(a). On the other hand, if the discriminant is negative then the square root cannot be taken in real numbers. In that case there are no real roots for the quadratic and we have Figure 1(c). Of course, you know that there are complex roots, which we can use mechanically but not graphically.

Exercises

4.   What happens if $a < 0$?
      What happens if $a = 0$?

5.   How do you get on with the cubic $y = ax^3 + bx^2 + cx + d$?

For polynomials in general, that is, anything of the form $ax^n + bx^{n-1} + \dots + p$, there are a couple of strategies that you can use. First of all, if the polynomial $p(x)$ has roots $r_1, r_2, \dots, r_n$, then $p(x) = a(x - r_1)(x - r_2) \dots (x - r_n)$.

Specifically, if the cubic $y = ax^3 + bx^2 + cx + d$ has three roots r_1, r_2, r_3, then

$$ax^3 + bx^2 + cx + d = a(x - r_1)(x - r_2)(x - r_3)$$
$$= a\left[x^3 - (r_1 + r_2 + r_3)x^2 + (r_1 r_2 + r_2 r_3 + r_3 r_1)x - r_1 r_2 r_3\right].$$

Since this relationship must be true for all values of x, we can equate the coefficients of like terms on opposite sides of the equal sign and obtain the equations

$$r_1 + r_2 + r_3 = -\frac{b}{a}$$

$$r_1 r_2 + r_2 r_3 + r_3 r_1 = \frac{c}{a}$$

$$r_1 r_2 r_3 = -\frac{d}{a},$$

and, if we can solve these equations, we have the roots.

Exercises

6.   Form the set of equations that relates the roots of $y = ax^4 + bx^3 + cx^2 + dx + e$ with the coefficients of the polynomial.

7.   Repeat exercise 6 for $y = ax^5 + bx^4 + cx^3 + dx^2 + ex + f$.

You should be able to see that the constant term in the polynomial is a times $(-r_1)(-r_2) \dots (-r_n) = (-1)^n r_1 r_2 \dots r_n$. There are similar expressions for the coefficients of $x, x^2, \dots x^{n-1}$ in terms of the roots. Sometimes this approach to roots is helpful.

Second, though, it's worth noticing that $p(r_1) = 0$, $p(r_2) = 0$, ..., $p(r_n) = 0$. It's sometimes possible to guess roots. If you think α is a root, replace x everywhere in $p(x)$ by α. If you get $p(\alpha) = 0$, then your guess was correct. [You probably know of this property as the Factor Theorem.]

I must say that this method is most useful when the roots are integers, because you can guess what they might be from the factors in the constant term of the polynomial.

Exercise
8. Find the roots of the following polynomials:

   (i) $x^2 + x - 30$;   (ii) $x^3 + 2x - x - 2$;

   (iii) $4x^4 - 1$;   (iv) $3x^4 - 22x^3 + 57x^2 - 62x + 24$.

Other equations come in the simultaneous variety with more than one variable. A technique that works in a lot of cases is to try to reduce the number of variables. With a bit of luck, the first equation will allow you to find one variable in terms of all the others. You can then substitute for this variable in all the other equations. Keep doing this until you have one equation in one unknown. Then you're back to where we were earlier in the chapter, trying to find the roots of a polynomial.

A second technique that frequently helps is to eliminate the constants by combining equations. This allows for an expression that often can be factored.

4.3   *Essential Skills*

As in other chapters, we provide a list of things that might be useful in solving problems in this chapter. If there's nothing here that seems to help then have a look at the corresponding lists in earlier chapters. Some of these earlier ideas may well be just what you want.

Factorisation

$$x^2 - y^2 = (x - y)(x + y)$$

$$x^3 - y^3 = (x - y)(x^2 + xy + y^2)$$

$$x^4 - y^4 = (x - y)(x^3 + x^2 y + xy^2 + y^3) \quad \text{or} \quad (x^2 - y^2)(x^2 + y^2) = (x - y)(x + y)(x^2 + y^2).$$

This pattern continues. Try a couple more to convince yourself.

Finding Roots

The Remainder Theorem   If $p(x)$ is a polynomial, then the remainder on dividing $p(x)$ by $x - \alpha$ is $p(\alpha)$.

The Factor Theorem   The value z is a root of the polynomial $p(x)$ if and only if $p(z) = 0$.

The roots of the quadratic equation $ax^2 + bx + c = 0$ are given by $x = \dfrac{-b \pm \sqrt{b^2 - 4ac}}{2a}$.

The roots $r_1, r_2, ..., r_n$ of a polynomial $p(x)$ with leading coefficient a, can be found from the coefficients of the polynomial in the following way:

$$\frac{\text{constant value}}{a} = (-1)^n r_1, r_2, ..., r_n$$

$$\frac{\text{coefficient of } x}{a} = \frac{r_1 r_2 \cdots r_n}{r_1} + \frac{r_1 r_2 \cdots r_n}{r_2} + \frac{r_1 r_2 \cdots r_n}{r_3} + ... + \frac{r_1 r_2 \cdots r_n}{r_n}$$

$$\frac{\text{coefficient of } x^2}{a} = (-1)^n \left\{ \frac{r_1 r_2 \cdots r_n}{r_1 r_2} + \frac{r_1 r_2 \cdots r_n}{r_1 r_3} + ... + \frac{r_1 r_2 \cdots r_n}{r_n - 1 r_2} \right\}$$

The pattern continues. It might be valuable to write this down precisely for a polynomial of degree 3 and for one of degree 4.

A useful idea. If $\beta < \gamma$, $p(\beta) > 0$ and $p(\gamma) < 0$, then there exists a root α if $p(x)$ between β and γ.

4.4   *Problem Solving Skills*

When I tried some of the problems in this chapter for the first time I had trouble getting my head around what was asked. In the clown problem, for instance, I completely misunderstood what was required. It wasn't until I went back a second time that I really got the hang of it. Hence read the questions carefully and try to absorb all the information they contain before you start work on the problem. You may find it useful to use a marker pen to highlight key pieces of information. You will sometimes need to go back and read the question in mid-problem solving to check that you're still on the right track. You should **always** read the question again at the end to make sure you answered the question that was being asked.

While we're on the end-game, sometimes after you've made your first solution attempt and have found the right answer, you may have sufficient insight into the problem to find an alternative solution. Sometimes this new solution will appear to be "nicer" in some respect than your first solution.

The other thing I'd encourage you to do if you're stuck is to have a guess. You'll remember we did this in section 1 with p and s. Your guess may not lead you anywhere, but then again it might. Often your "feelings" for a problem can be justified. Try to justify them before looking at the solution we have provided.

You'll also find that drawing a diagram is still a valuable thing to do from time to time, even though this chapter is entitled "Algebra". Many word problems rely on a diagram to provide the initial inspiration required to solve them.

Some of the problems will remind you of others that you've successfully negotiated here and in earlier chapters. Never be afraid to try a technique that you've found did the job in another occasion.

One or two of the problems in the chapter might be helped along by the use of a table. And if some of the numbers are a little high, use smaller ones until you find some inspiration.

4.5   A Bit of Chaos

We thought, that is mathematicians thought, that they had gotten on top of quadratics until Iteration came along and wrecked our intuition. Iteration just means repeating things over and over again. For instance, take x^2. If we start with $x_0 = 0.5$, we get 0.25. Now put the 0.25 back in the square again. Squaring 0.25 gives 0.0625. If we square 0.0625 we get something even smaller. As we do it again and again we gradually find the numbers that we are producing are approaching zero.

That's not all that is interesting, so try the following examples.

Exercises
9.   Iterate the following starting at the given initial values, x_0:

    (i) $2.5x(1-x)$; $x_0 = 0.1$ and 0.5;   (ii) $3.1x(1-x)$; $x_0 = 0.1$ and 0.2;

    (iii) $4x(1-x)$; $x_0 = 0.2$ and 0.21;   (iv) $2x(1-x)$; $x_0 = 0.5$.

10.   Solve the following equation for x

    $x = \lambda x(1-x)$.

The quadratic $x = \lambda x(1-x)$ has some very surprising properties. As you have seen from Exercise 9, for some values of λ the iteration appears to converge to a fixed value. For other values of λ the iterations oscillate as they converge to two fixed values. For still other values of λ, the quadratic oscillates all over the place.

Where there is convergence to a fixed value, we can find that value by solving $x = \lambda x(1-x)$ which you did in Exercise 13 to give $x = 0$ or $\dfrac{\lambda - 1}{\lambda}$. Now you get back precisely those values. Iteration just keeps them repeating. Depending on λ, the quadratic may or may not converge to fixed points.

If we let $f(x) = \lambda x(1-x)$, then the fixed points are given by $f(x) = x$. Another interesting set of points is obtained by putting $f(f(x)) = x$. This gives us **period 2 points**.

$$f(f(x)) = \lambda f(x)(1 - f(x))$$

$$= \lambda[\lambda x(1-x)][1 - \lambda x(1-x)].$$

Exercise
11.   Solve $f(f(x)) = x$.

If the conditions are right, as they are with $\lambda = 3.1$, iteration never converges to a single point but oscillates backwards and forwards between two values - the period 2 points.

You might try your luck at solving $f^3(x) = x$ and find period 3 points, but be warned; the algebra is tricky.

The thing that is interesting about $\lambda x(1-x)$ for some values of λ is the behaviour of neighbouring initial points. If a and b are close together, what happens when you iterate starting with $x = a$ may be quite different than what happens when you start with $x = b$. You should have found this when you used $\lambda = 4$ in Exercise 9(iii). This unexpected behaviour is called **chaos**. It turns out that chaos is more common than we expected.

Problems

If you get stuck on a problem, there are some hints beginning on page 114.

1. Solve the system of equations:
    $$x^2 - y^2 = 21$$
    $$x - y = 3$$

2. Given that $x = -2$ is a solution of the equation $x^3 - 7x - 6 = 0$, determine the other solutions.

3. Determine all values of x, y, z satisfying the system of equations
    $$x + 2y - 3z = -1$$
    $$2x + 5y + 12z = 9$$
    $$3x + 6y - 3z = 1$$

4. The sequence of numbers $a_1, a_2, a_3, ...$ satisfies $\dfrac{a_m}{a_n} = \dfrac{m}{n}$ for every pair of positive integers m and n. If $a_3 = 5$, determine a_{20}.

5. Solve $x^2 + xy = 3$
    $$3x^2 + 2xy - 2y^2 = 7$$

6. Solve the system of equations:
    $$7x - 4y + 8z = 37$$
    $$3x + 2y - 4z = 1$$
    $$x^2 + y^2 + z^2 = 14$$

7. Determine the values of m for which the graph of the parabola $y = x^2 + mx + 16$ is always above the x-axis.

8. The graph of a quadratic function is given in the diagram. Determine the area of the shaded rectangle.

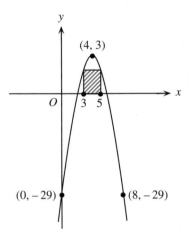

9. Let A and B be the points of intersection of the parabola $y = x^2 - 8x + 7$ and the x-axis, and let C be the vertex of the parabola. Determine the area of triangle ABC.

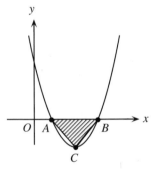

10. Determine the number of integer values of x such that $\sqrt{2 - (1 + x)^2}$ is an integer.

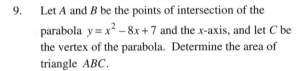

11. Starting at 10:00 a.m. from A, a runner runs due north at a speed of 10 km/h. Starting 30 minutes later from B, which is 25 km east of A, a cyclist travels northwest at a constant speed. The runner and the cyclist arrive at the same point at the same time. Determine the speed of the bicycle, expressing your answer correct to one decimal place.

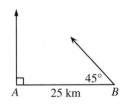

12. Determine all real values of p and r which satisfy the system of equations:

$$p + pr + pr^2 = 26$$
$$p^2r + p^2r^2 + p^2r^3 = 156$$

13. In a parade, a clown walks at a constant rate of 1.6 m/s along the edge of a rectangular platform with sides 6 m long and ends 2 m long. The platform is moving in a straight line at a rate of 1 m/s. At time $t = 0$ seconds, the clown starts from the midpoint of one end of the platform. He throws one candy to the crowd at each of the times $t = 1, 2, 3, 4, \ldots$ seconds, but only if he is walking along a side at that time. If the platform travels 6 km, how many candies does the clown throw to the crowd?

14. Solve for x: $\left(x^2 - 3x + 1\right)^2 - 3\left(x^2 - 3x + 1\right) + 1 = x$.

15. Determine the value of k so that the parabola whose equation is $y = x^2 + 2x + 2k - 3$ will have its vertex on the x-axis.

16. A freight train is 27 minutes late when it makes its usual trip between City A and City B at an average speed of 56 km/h. For another trip between City A and City B, the train is 42 minutes late when its average speed is 54 km/h. What is the distance between City A and City B?

    There are two approaches to this problem. Solution 1 uses the fact that the difference in the times is 15 minutes. Solution 2 uses the fact that the distance is always the same.

17. Nine large hoses can fill a swimming pool in four hours and six small hoses can fill the same swimming pool in eight hours. How many hours will it take four large hoses and eight small hoses working together to fill the swimming pool?

18. A besieged fortress is held by 5700 men, who have provisions for 66 days. If the garrison loses 20 men each day, for how many days can the provisions hold out?

19. Farmer Haas has 100 m of fencing to enclose a rectangular pasture. One side of the pasture can include all or part of one side of his barn. If the side of his barn is 40 m, determine the maximum area of pasture he can enclose.

20. In the equation $ax^4 + bx^3 + cx^2 - 630 = 0$, a, b and c are integers. Determine the value of p if p is a prime number which is a root of the equation.

Chapter 5   Exponentials and Logarithms

5.1   Background

In this chapter we will assume that you know the basic rules for operating with exponents and logarithms. We will concentrate our efforts on developing exponential and logarithmic functions and on the various problems that require their use. Let's begin with an example that ultimately leads to some interesting results.

Example 1
Marilyn has invested $1000 at 10% compounded annually. How much will her $1000 have grown to after 6 years?

The first question I want to ask Marilyn is where did she find someone to give her 10% interest? Rates like that have not been around for awhile, though no doubt they'll come again. Let us start by calculating this one step at a time.

At the end of the first year she'll get $1000 \times 10\% = \$1000 \times 0.1 = \$100$ in interest. So the accumulated value of her investment will be $\$1000 + \$100 = \$1100$. We could find this total in one step by just evaluating $\$1000(1 + 0.1) = \$1000(1.1) = \$1100$.

At the end of the second year the accumulated value will be
$\$1000(1.1)(1 + 0.1) = \$1000(1.1)^2 = \$1210$.

I think you can see what is going on here. At the end of six years Marilyn's investment will be worth $\$1000(1.1)^6 = \$1771.56$.

Now let's change the conditions a bit. Suppose Marilyn is able to invest the $1000 for 6 years at 10% compounded quarterly, that is, every three months. To calculate this amount we use a rate of $\frac{1}{4} \times 10\% = 2.5\%$, and at the same time note that there are $6 \times 4 = 24$ periods of time when the interest is calculated. Then the accumulated value of the investment is
$\$1000(1.025)^{24} = \$1809$ (to the nearest dollar). So it is to Marilyn's advantage to have interest compounded more often.

Perhaps we should calculate what happens when interest is compounded every day. After 6 years the accumulated value of her investment would be

$$\$1000\left(1 + \frac{0.1}{365}\right)^{6 \times 365} \quad \text{(we are ignoring leap years)}$$

$$= \$1000(1.000274)^{2190}$$
$$= \$1822. \quad \text{(to the nearest dollar)}.$$

Again we see that compounding more frequently increases the value of the investment but the increase is not as great as we might guess.

We can generalize these results. If $P is invested for t years at a rate of $R\%$ per annum, compounded n times a year, the accumulated value of the investment is given by

$$A = P\left(1+\frac{r}{n}\right)^{nt}, \text{ where } r = \frac{R}{100}. \text{ (The use of } r = \frac{R}{100} \text{ expresses interest as a decimal).}$$

Is it possible to calculate interest continually? Surely this would make Marilyn's investment grow to some maximum value.

Example 2
If Marilyn invests $1000 at 10% per annum for one year and the interest is calculated every nth of a year, she will have

$$1000\left[1+\frac{0.1}{n}\right]^{n} \text{ at the end of the year.}$$

If the interest is compounded continually, she'll have

$$\lim_{n\to\infty}\left[1+\frac{0.1}{n}\right]^{n} \text{ at the end of the first year.}$$

To estimate this amount we could complete the table below.

n	10	100	1000	10 000
$\$1000\left(1+\frac{0.1}{n}\right)^{n}$	$1104.62	$1105.12	$1105.17	$1105.17

After rounding off the answer to the nearest cent it appears that the accumulated value is approaching a limit somewhere around $1105.17.

It turns out that $\lim_{n\to\infty}\left[1+\frac{1}{n}\right]^{n}$ does exist. It's equal to a number called e, after the mathematician Euler. The number e is irrational with an approximate value of 2.71828.

So

$$\lim_{n\to\infty}\left[1+\frac{1}{n}\right]^{n} = e \cong 2.71828.$$

Interesting enough,

$$\lim_{n\to\infty}\left[1+\frac{x}{n}\right]^{n} = e^{x}. \text{ (Pronounced "e to the x")}$$

In example 2 we want $1000\lim_{n\to\infty}\left[1+\frac{0.1}{n}\right]^{n} = \$1000e^{0.1}$

$$= \$1000(2.71828)^{0.1}$$
$$= \$1105.17.$$

So our estimate of the accumulated value of Marilyn's investment using the table was right on (to the nearest cent). Of course, all of this arithmetic means we need a calculator, or a computer, if we want answers quickly.

Exercises
1. How much will Marilyn's investment have become after 1 year, given that interest is compounded monthly?
2. How much greater will the accumulated value of Marilyn's investment be after 6 years if interest is compounded continually rather than annually?
3. What would you expect the value of e^0 to be? Is this the answer you get when you put $x = 0$ into the limit expression for e?
4. What can be said about e^x for $x > 1$ and for $x < 0$?
5. What was Euler's first name? Where and when did he live?

5.2   *Essential Skills*

In this chapter, there are a number of mathematical skills that you will need in order to be able to do the problems at the end. Check through the list that I've written out below and make sure you are comfortable with everything. If you get stuck on any of the later problems, don't feel bashful about coming back to this section to seek inspiration.

The exponential function, $y = e^x$.
Since $0 < e^x < 1$ for $x < 0$ and $e^x > 1$ for $x > 0$, then e^x is never zero or negative.

The graph of $y = e^x$ is

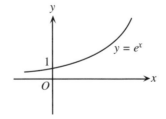

Operations with e^x satisfy the usual laws of exponents:

$$e^x e^y = e^{x+y}$$

$$\left(e^x\right)^y = e^{xy}$$

$$\frac{e^x}{e^y} = e^{x-y}$$

$$e^0 = 1.$$

The natural logarithm function, $y = \log_e x.$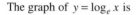

If $r = e^s$, then we say that $s = \log_e r.$

If $0 < r < 1$, $\log_e r < 0$ and if $r > 1$, $\log_e r > 0.$

If $r = 1$, $s = 0$; so $\log_e 1 = 0.$

If $r \le 0$, then $\log_e r$ does not exist.

The graph of $y = \log_e x$ is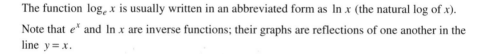

The function $\log_e x$ is usually written in an abbreviated form as $\ln x$ (the natural log of x).

Note that e^x and $\ln x$ are inverse functions; their graphs are reflections of one another in the line $y = x.$

In general, $\log_e rs = \log_e r + \log_e s$

$$\log_e r^s = s \log_e r,$$

and $\log_e e = 1.$

Other bases

For any positive number a, a^x is defined. The graph of $y = a^x$ can be any one of the three below.

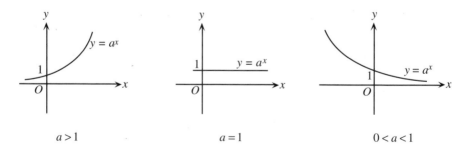

       $a > 1$ $a = 1$ $0 < a < 1$

As with e^x,

$$a^0 = 1$$
$$a^x a^y = a^{x+y}$$
$$\left(a^x\right)^y = a^{xy}$$
$$\frac{a^x}{a^y} = a^{x-y}.$$

Now we can also work with $y = \log_a x$.

If $r = a^s$, then $s = \log_a r$. Hence $\log_a 1 = 0$. But the graph of $y = \log_a x$, like the graph of $y = a^x$, depends upon the value of a. The three possible graphs are shown below.

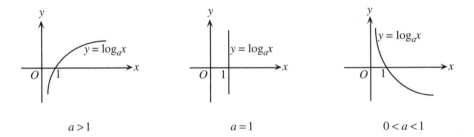

$$a > 1 \qquad\qquad\qquad a = 1 \qquad\qquad\qquad 0 < a < 1$$

In general, $\log_a rs = \log_a r + \log_a s$
$$\log_a rs = s \log_a r$$
$$\log_a \frac{r}{s} = \log_a r - \log_a s$$
and $\log_a a = 1$.

Links between bases

$$\log_a x = \frac{\log_b x}{\log_b a}.$$

In particular, $\log_e x = \dfrac{\log_b x}{\log_b e}$

$$\log_a x = \frac{\log_e x}{\log_e a}$$

and $\log_a b = \dfrac{1}{\log_b a}.$

5.3   *Problem Solving Skills*

I'll now go through some of the problem solving skills which are particularly important and then do some problems which might help you solve some of the questions we pose in the latter part of the chapter.

Algebra
Most of the questions in this chapter will rely for a solution on your ability to manipulate symbols in one way or another. You'll find that you'll need to use many of the tricks that were introduced in Chapter 4. So be on the look out for factorisation and so on.

Have I seen something like this before?
This is always a good problem solving technique. The more problems you do, the more likely it is that the current problem is like one you did a little while ago. If you get stuck on a problem later in this chapter, think back to things that you've done earlier in the book. You may well find a clue there that will let you solve another problem.

Exponential versus Logarithms
One of the crucial decisions that you'll need to make in many of the problems is whether you should work in logarithms. That means that you may want to do everything in the form a^x. Sometimes even though there's a $\log_a x$ in the problem it's going to be better to change everything to the exponential form.
On the other hand, some problems are more easily done with logarithms. This may be obvious on some occasions when there are lots of logs around.

Some Examples
I'll do a couple of examples here which may help you on your way.

Example 1
If $\log_3\left(\log_4 a^3\right)=1$, find a.

Comment
Is there anything that we can do with the logarithms? What do we know about logarithms that could help us here?

How about $\log_3 3=1$ or $\log_4 a^3 = 3\log_4 a$?

Solution
Maybe we can use both of these facts. Since $\log_3 3=1$, we know that $\log_4 a^3$ must equal 3. Hence $\log_4 a^3 = 3$

$$3\log_4 a = 3$$
$$\log_4 a = 1.$$
Therefore $a = 4$.

Example 2

Solve the equation $e^x + 1 = 6e^{-x}$.

Comment

It's not immediately obvious what to do here. Taking logs of both sides doesn't seem to simplify things. Wait a minute though. What if we multiplied through by e^x? Wouldn't that give us a quadratic equation in e^x? Let's try it.

Solution

$$e^{2x} + e^x = 6$$

That might look more presentable with the 6 on the other side of the equation.

$$e^{2x} + e^x - 6 = 0.$$

If we put $y = e^x$, we have a quadratic equation

$$y^2 + y - 6 = 0.$$

Hence $(y+3)(y-2) = 0$.

So $y = -3$ or $y = 2$. But if $y = -3$, then $e^x = -3$.

Since e^x is always positive, there is no x such that $e^x = -3$.

On the other hand, if $y = 2$, then $e^x = 2$. Taking logs of both sides tells us that $x = \log_e 2$.

Now we can either be happy with that exact solution or use a calculator to find x to some 5 or 6 decimal place. Personally, I like the $x = \log_e 2$ form.

Example 3

Solve the following equation for y in terms of x, $2^{x+3y} = 8^{x-3y}$.

Comment

The x's and y's are no good to us as exponents. The only way to be able to manipulate them usefully is to get them "down". This can be done by taking logs of both sides.

Solution

$$\log 2^{x+3y} = \log 8^{x-3y}$$

Therefore $(x+3y)\log 2 = (x-3y)\log 8$.

Ah, but $\qquad \log 8 = \log 2^3 = 3\log 2$.

So $\qquad (x+3y)\log 2 = 3(x-3y)\log 2$.

The problem is essentially solved now.

$$x + 3y = 3x - 9y$$

Hence $12y = 2x$ or $y = \dfrac{1}{6}x$.

Comment

Actually I now see an easier way.

Since $8 = 2^3$, $8^{x-3y} = 2^{3(x-3y)}$.

This gives $2^{x+3y} = 2^{3(x-3y)}$.

So $x + 3y = 3(x - 3y)$, which leads again to $y = \frac{1}{6}x$.

5.4   *Application and Avoidance*

One of the most common applications of exponentials is in the area of growth and decay. Given the right conditions, some things grow exponentially. This can be seen in bacteria on a Petri dish. Given sufficient nutrients the number of cells on the dish increases exponentially with time. We have an equation that looks like $n = n_0 e^{kt}$.

Here n is the number of cells at time t, n_0 the initial number (at $t = 0$) and k is some constant. The graph of such a situation is shown in Figure 1.

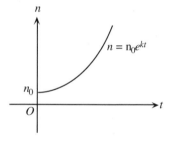

Figure 1

It's pretty clear though that exponential growth cannot continue indefinitely. As the nutrient supply in the Petri dish decreases, the number of cells tends to go toward some limit. This is modelled better by the equation

$$n = \frac{Ae^{kt}}{1 + e^{kt}}.$$

The graph of this is shown in Figure 2.

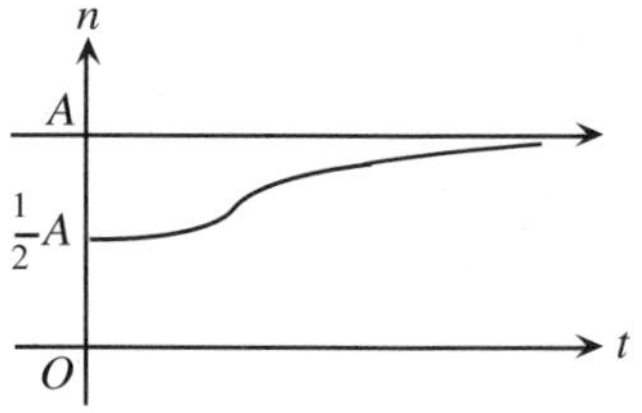

Figure 2

The experimental growth represented in Figure 1 can actually happen in animal populations. There is the famous example of deer being released on an island away from predators of any kind. For some time their population growth was literally exponential, then the food supply on the island was completely exhausted and the deer all died over one winter.

Death, or rather decay, is at the centre of radio-active carbon dating. Because radio-active substances decay at a rate proportional to the amount present, the amount present satisfies an equation like

$$r = r_0 e^{-kt}.$$

Here r is the amount at time t, r_0 is the initial amount of the radio-active substance and k gives the rate of decay. Some elements have radio-active isotopes. The fraction of radio-active isotope in naturally occurring matter is known. By measuring the amount of inert and radio-active isotopes in a particular sample and knowing the original fraction, the time taken for the decay to take place can be calculated. Hence the age of objects can be determined.

Exponentials therefore have their uses but there are occasions when they are definitely a bad thing. One situation where we do not want exponential behaviour is in computer programming. It would be nice if computer programs could do their job efficiently and as quickly as possible.

Suppose you have a program which is generating examples of some type for you. As the size of the examples increases the time for the program to run will also increase. But the program will be able to generate fairly large examples if the program is somehow polynomial in, say, the size of the example. If the running time is exponential in the size of the example, it will take considerably longer to run them if it is polynomial. Consequently it will only be feasible to compute smaller sized examples.

This idea has led to the concepts of P and NP. The P stands for **polynomial** while the NP stands for **non-deterministic** polynomial.

Let's think about this in terms of an example. A **graph** is a collection of vertices (dots) and edges (lines joining two dots). I've given a few examples in Figure 3.

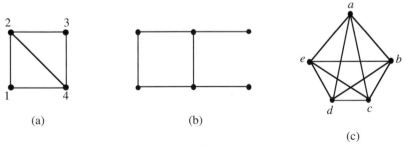

(a) (b)

(c)

Figure 3

One of the important problems in graph theory is to find a Hamiltonian cycle in a graph. Such a cycle is one which goes through every vertex of the graph once and only once, ending at the vertex where it started. There are Hamiltonian cycles in Figure 3(a) and Figure 3(c). In Figure 3(a), 1 to 2 to 3 to 4 to 1 is a Hamiltonian cycle, while a to c to e to b to d to a is a Hamiltonian cycle in Figure 3(c).

The Hamiltonian cycle problem is related to the Travelling Salesperson problem so solving it has economic ramifications. (In the Travelling Salesperson problem, we are interested in finding the most efficient route for a salesperson who has to visit a number of customers, and get back home). It doesn't at the moment look as if the Hamiltonian problem is P. In other words, there seems to be no program that will decide whether or not a graph on n vertices is Hamiltonian, where the program runs in polynomial time depending on the number of vertices of the graph.

Finding whether a graph is Hamiltonian appears to be NP. Actually defining NP is beyond the scope of this book. However, we do know that the Hamiltonian problem is **NP-complete**. This means that if the Hamiltonian problem is NP, then so are a whole class of other problems.

What is interesting about P and NP is that no one has been able to prove that they are different. People believe that NP problems are not P but there is as yet no way to show this. It's one of the outstanding, interesting, and important problems in an area of mathematics/computing called **complexity theory**. You might be interested in reading more about this.

Problems

If you get stuck on a problem, there are some hints beginning on page 115.

1.   Determine the value of each of the expressions:

   (a) 5^{2x-1}, given that $5^x = 15$.

   (b) $\log_3\left(\dfrac{\sqrt{3}}{2}\right) - \log_3\left(\dfrac{1}{2}\right)$.

   (c) $\log_8 18$ in terms of x, where $\log_8 3 = x$.

2.   Solve each of the equations for x, where x is a real number.

   (a) $7^{x+2} - 7^x = 48\sqrt{7}$.

   (b) $3^{2x} + 3^x = 20$.

   (c) $\dfrac{1}{2^{1990}} - \dfrac{1}{2^{1991}} = 2^x$.

3. The roots of $9x^2 - 28x + 3 = 0$ are r and s. Find the value of $\log_3 r + \log_3 s$.

4. The graph of the function defined by $y = \log_a x$ is shown. What is the value of a?

5. If $\log_x 2 = a$ and $\log_x 3 = b$, find the value of $\log_x\left(\frac{9}{2}x^2\right)$ in terms of a and b.

6. Solve the system of equations
$$3^{2x-y} = 27$$
$$2^{3x+2y} = 32$$

7. Solve the equation $\log_2(3x+4) - \log_2(x-3) = 3$.

8. What is the sum of the series $\log_{10}\left(\frac{3}{2}\right) + \log_{10}\left(\frac{4}{3}\right) + \log_{10}\left(\frac{5}{4}\right) + \cdots + \log_{10}\left(\frac{200}{199}\right)$.

9. If $f(x) = 49^{3x}$ and $g(x) = \log_7 x$, what is the value of $g[f(100)]$?

10. If $\log x^2 = a$, $\log y^3 = b$ and $\log xy = c$, prove that $6c = 3a + 2b$.

11. Solve the equation $\log_2\left(9 - 2^x\right) = 3 - x$.

12. Prove that $\dfrac{e^{-x}}{e^{-x}+1} + \dfrac{e^x}{e^x+1} = 1$.

13. Given that $\lim\limits_{n\to\infty}\left(1+\frac{1}{n}\right)^n = e$, prove that $\lim\limits_{n\to\infty}\left(1+\frac{x}{n}\right)^n = e^x$.

14. Determine the largest integer value of n so that $\left(\frac{21}{20}\right)^n < 100$.

15. If $\log_x a = m$ and $\log_y a = n$, find the value of $\log_{\frac{x}{y}} a$ in terms of m and n.

16. If $S = \dfrac{1}{\log_2 e} + \dfrac{1}{\log_3 e} + \dfrac{1}{\log_4 e} + \cdots + \dfrac{1}{\log_{20} e}$, prove that $S = \ln(20!)$.

17. In a lottery, all prizes are powers of \$11; that is, only \$1, \$11, \$121, ... are possible prizes. There can be more than one prize of any given amount. It is not necessary that there be a prize for every power of 11. If the total sum of all prizes is to be exactly one million dollars, what is the minimum number of prizes in the lottery?

18. Prove that there is a positive integer n such that $1995^{1994} < 1994^n < 1995^{1995}$.

19. Another way to express e is to write it as an infinite series, namely,

$e = 1 + \dfrac{1}{1!} + \dfrac{1}{2!} + \dfrac{1}{3!} + \dfrac{1}{4!} + \cdots + \dfrac{1}{n!} + \cdots$. We won't attempt to prove that this series is

equivalent to $\lim\limits_{n \to \infty} \left(1 + \dfrac{1}{n}\right)^n$, but you might like to try to prove that e is irrational using this

series.

Chapter 6   Trigonometry

6.1   Measuring Buildings

I think it was the physicist Feynman, though I may be wrong, who posed the problem of measuring the height of a building, given a barometer. It turns out that there are a number of ways of doing this. For instance, you might get a long piece of string and tie it to the top of the barometer. If you let it hang from the top of the building, you could make a knot in the string when the barometer touches the ground. At your convenience you could measure the string and you would then have the height of the building.

Exercises
1.   Who was Richard Feynman? (You might try reading "Surely You're Joking, Mr. Feynman!" and "What Do You Care What Other People Think?" by Richard P. Feynman.)
2.   How do you think you were supposed to measure the height of a building using a barometer?
3.   Find another way of determining the height of a building using a barometer.

There are, in fact, several ways of getting a building's height with a barometer. You could measure the barometer's length. Then you, or Spiderman, could scale the exterior of the building, carefully using the barometer to measure your progress.

Alternatively you could stick the barometer into the ground and lie down and "sight" the top of the building.

If you carefully measure a few things you can find the height of the building again. In using this method you don't **have** to use angles but using angles is possible, even if you temporarily mislay the barometer.

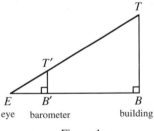

Figure 1

It turns out that the ratio of BT to BE is actually dependent on the angle θ. The same can be said for $\dfrac{BT}{ET}$ and $\dfrac{BE}{ET}$. We define functions called sine, cosine and tangent, such that

$$\sin \theta = \frac{BT}{ET}, \cos \theta = \frac{BE}{ET} \text{ and } \tan \theta = \frac{BT}{BE}.$$

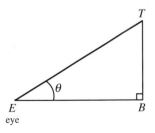

Figure 2

The sine, cosine and tangent functions, which we often abbreviate to sin, cos, and tan, are called **trigonometric functions**. As we have introduced them in Figure 2 they are only defined for angles θ such that $0° \le \theta \le 90°$ although we have to fudge things a bit at $0°$ and $90°$, especially for tan $90°$! But all of these trigonometric functions are defined over a much wider range of values. To see how this is done, look at Figure 3.

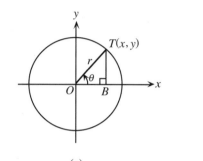

(a)

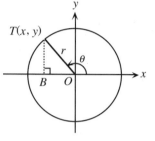

(b)

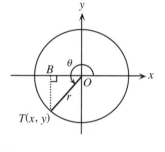

(c)

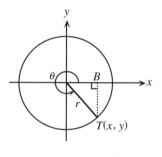

(d)

Figure 3

In Figure 3(a), $\sin \theta = \dfrac{BT}{OT} = \dfrac{y}{r}$ where $r = \sqrt{x^2 + y^2}$. That obviously fits in with the definition from Figure 2. However, we push the definition further by deciding to use $\sin \theta = \dfrac{BT}{OT}$ no matter what quadrant the angle θ is in. There's nothing unusual then, for θ in Figure 3(b). But we have to be careful in Figure 3(c) to remember that y is negative, so in this quadrant, $\sin \theta$ is negative. The same thing is true for θ in the fourth quadrant. Since r is the distance from the centre O we keep that always positive.

Now we can make completely general definitions for our functions based on the angle θ defined by a point $T(x, y)$ on the circle and the positive x-axis:

$$\sin \theta = \frac{y}{r} \quad ; \quad \cos \theta = \frac{x}{r} \quad ; \quad \tan \theta = \frac{y}{x}, \text{ where } r = \sqrt{x^2 + y^2} \text{ is the radius of the circle.}$$

Example

If we select $T_1(1, 1)$ in the first quadrant, $\theta = 45°$ and $r = \sqrt{2}$.

So $\sin 45° = \dfrac{1}{\sqrt{2}}$, $\cos 45° = \dfrac{1}{\sqrt{2}}$, and $\tan 45° = 1$.

But now we can see all kinds of repetition as illustrated in Figure 4. For example,

$$\sin 225° = \sin(180° + 45°) = -\frac{1}{\sqrt{2}}$$

and $\quad \sin 315° = \sin(360° - 45°) = -\dfrac{1}{\sqrt{2}}$.

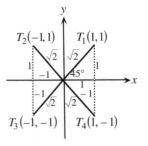

Figure 4

Exercises

4. (a) Find a right-angled triangle with angles $45°$ and $45°$. Then calculate
    - (i) $\sin 45°$;
    - (ii) $\sin 135°$;
    - (iii) $\sin 315°$;
    - (iv) $\cos 225°$;
    - (v) $\cos 135°$;
    - (vi) $\tan 45°$;
    - (vii) $\tan 315°$.

    (b) Now draw a right-angled triangle with angles $30°$ and $60°$. Calculate
    - (i) $\sin 60°$;
    - (ii) $\cos 60°$;
    - (iii) $\sin 120°$;
    - (iv) $\sin 300°$;
    - (v) $\cos 150°$;
    - (vi) $\cos 270°$;
    - (vii) $\tan 120°$;
    - (viii) $\tan 330°$;
    - (ix) $\tan 480°$.

5. Figure 2 is fine for measuring things where it is easy to find the distance BE. In the case of a mountain this is somewhat difficult. How could you find the height of a mountain using trigonometry?

So far we have only used degrees to measure angles. Another type of measure is **radians**. We define one radian to be the angle subtended at the centre of a circle by an arc equal in length to the radius. Probably this is easier to see than hear. Look at the diagram in Figure 5. The arc of the circle "defined" by θ is length r. So we say that $\theta = 1$ radian.

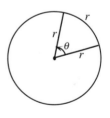

Figure 5

It should be straightforward to calculate a few basic angles in terms of radians using Figure 5.

Exercises

6. Show that an angle of $360°$ is also of size 2π radians.

7. What is $180°$ in radians? How about $45°$?

8. What is $\dfrac{1}{3}\pi$ radians in degrees? What is $\dfrac{7\pi}{6}$ radians in degrees?

One thing that is useful to know about any function is its graph. Having a picture in our mind of the function often makes it easier to use the function. So what does the graph of $y = \sin \theta$ look like? A good way to start on this is to plot various points. It's always a good start to find points where the graph crosses the axes. So what is y when $\theta = 0$ and what is θ when $y = 0$?

The first of these is easy. If $\theta = 0$, we are measuring a triangle where the side opposite is zero. Hence $\sin 0 = 0$. But what values of θ give $y = 0$? To check this out a quick look at Figure 3 is useful. We get $y = 0$ when $BT = 0$. This happens when $\theta = 0$, π, 2π, plus any positive or negative multiples of 2π.

Another thing that's worth knowing about $\sin \theta$ is that $\sin(-\theta) = -\sin \theta$. And the other useful thing to know about $\sin \theta$ is that is can never be bigger than 1 or smaller than -1. I'll let you ponder about those two points.

Anyway, combining all this information gives the graph of the sine function shown in Figure 6.

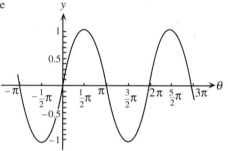

Figure 6

Exercises

9. (a) Prove that $\sin(-\theta) = -\sin \theta$.
    (b) Is $\cos(-\theta) = -\cos \theta$?
    (c) Is $\tan(-\theta) = -\tan \theta$?
10. (a) Why is $|\sin \theta| \le 1$?
    (b) Is it true that $|\cos \theta| \le 1$?
    (c) Is it true that $|\tan \theta| \le 1$?
11. Sketch the graphs of $y = \cos \theta$ and $y = \tan \theta$.
12. Sketch the following graphs:

   (i) $y = 3 \sin 2\theta$;   (ii) $y = \sin \dfrac{3\pi\theta}{4}$ (iii) $y = 1 + \cos \dfrac{\pi\theta}{2}$;

   (iv) $y = 1 - 2 \cos \theta$;   (v) $y = \tan(\theta - \pi)$;   (vi) $y = \left| \tan \dfrac{\pi\theta}{4} \right|$.

6.2 *Mathematical Skills*

This is the part of the chapter where I list all of the facts that I think you are likely to need to do the problems that lie ahead.

Basic Definitions

No matter how big the angle θ is, $\sin \theta = \frac{y}{r}$, $\cos \theta = \frac{x}{r}$,

$\tan \theta = \frac{y}{x}$, $\operatorname{cosec} \theta = \frac{r}{y}$, $\sec \theta = \frac{r}{x}$, $\cot \theta = \frac{x}{y}$.

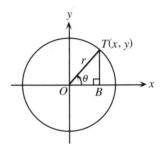

- θ is measured positively in a counter-clockwise direction from the positive x-axis (and so is negative when measured clockwise);
- $\operatorname{cosec} \theta$ is the cosecant of the angle θ and is the reciprocal of $\sin \theta$;
- $\sec \theta$ is the secant of the angle θ and is the reciprocal of $\cos \theta$;
- $\cot \theta$ is the cotangent of the angle θ and is the reciprocal of $\tan \theta$.

Basic Facts

$\sin (-\theta) = -\sin \theta$, $\cos (-\theta) = \cos \theta$, $\tan(-\theta) = -\tan \theta$,

$\sin (180° - \theta) = \sin \theta$, $\cos (360° - \theta) = \cos \theta$, $\tan (180° + \theta) = \tan \theta$.

$\sin \theta = \cos (90° - \theta)$, $\cos \theta = \sin (90° - \theta)$.

Since $x^2 + y^2 = r^2$, we have

$$\frac{x^2}{r^2} + \frac{y^2}{r^2} = 1.$$

Hence $\cos^2 \theta + \sin^2 \theta = 1$, for all values of θ.
It is also true that

$$\sin (A \pm B) = \sin A \cos B \pm \cos A \sin B,$$

$$\cos (A \pm B) = \cos A \cos B \mp \sin A \sin B, \text{ and}$$

$$\tan (A \pm B) = \frac{\tan A \pm \tan B}{1 \mp \tan A \tan B}.$$

By putting $A = B$, the above equations lead to the **double angle** formulas,

$$\sin 2A = 2 \sin A \cos A,$$

$$\cos 2A = \cos^2 A - \sin^2 B, \text{ and}$$

$$\tan 2A = \frac{2 \tan A}{1 - \tan^2 A}.$$

Using $\sin^2 A + \cos^2 A = 1$, the double angle formulas for cosine can also be written as

$$\cos 2A = 2\cos^2 A - 1, \text{ and}$$

$$\cos 2A = 1 - 2\sin^2 A.$$

From Section 1, we also know that 2π radians = 360 degrees.

From Chapter 2, we know the **sine** and **cosine rules** which state that in the triangle shown

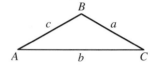

$$\frac{a}{\sin A} = \frac{b}{\sin B} = \frac{c}{\sin C}, \text{ and}$$

$$a^2 = b^2 + c^2 - 2bc \cos A.$$

Some Basic Triangles
It is worth remembering the sides of the following two right-angled triangles. These are useful for the values they provide for commonly used angles.

$$\sin 45° = \frac{1}{\sqrt{2}} = \cos 45°$$

$$\tan 45° = 1$$

$$\sin 30° = \frac{1}{2}, \qquad \sin 60° = \frac{\sqrt{3}}{2},$$

$$\cos 30° = \frac{\sqrt{3}}{2}, \qquad \cos 60° = \frac{1}{2},$$

$$\tan 30° = \frac{1}{\sqrt{3}}, \qquad \tan 60° = \sqrt{3}$$

Trigonometric Graphs
$y = \sin \theta$

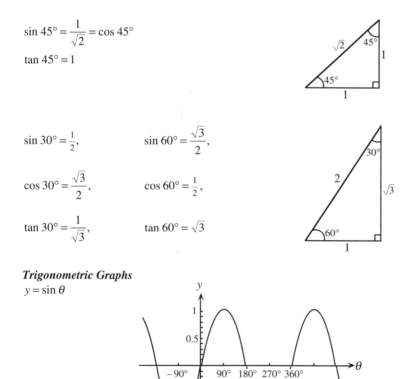

$y = \cos\theta$

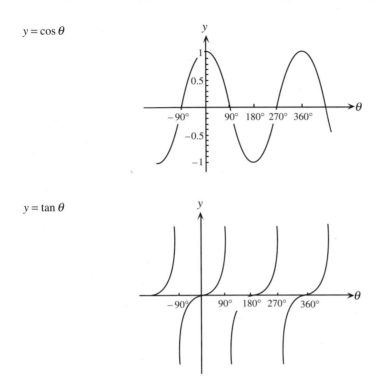

$y = \tan\theta$

Solving Triangles

To find angles and sides in a right-angled triangle, we can use the trigonometric ratios, provided we have sufficient information; all angles and sides can be determined if one side and one other angle are known or if two sides are known. To find angles and sides in *any* triangle, the sine and cosine rules can be used. All angles and sides can be determined if one side and two angles are known, if two sides and an angle are known, or if three sides are known.

Other Facts

Anything that occurred in previous chapters could be useful here. Such things as factorisation may come in handy.

6.3 Problem Solving Skills

The problems in this chapter fall roughly into four types. These are finding or using graphs of trigonometric functions, solving equations, solving equations to find length and/or ratios, and trigonometric identities.

In the graphical type problems it is important to draw a diagram; the sketch graph of the situation. To do this you will need to use mathematical skills from the first two sections of this chapter.

When solving equations it is useful to make use of things you have seen before. For instance, sometimes by manipulating the trigonometric functions, you can change the equation into a quadratic. From here you can either factorise or solve using the quadratic formula.

In cases where you are asked to find a length or a ratio, it is important to draw a diagram. Indeed, it is hard to see how these problems can be done without a diagram unless you have an exceptionally good imagination and memory.

To solve trigonometric identities requires some problem-solving skills. You have to prove that the left hand side of an equation is identical to the right hand side. So you have to guide the left hand side along, using your knowledge of trigonometric functions, until you get to the form of the right hand side. Sometimes this might prove difficult. You may only be able to see how to get the left hand side to a certain stage. If you get stuck, experiment with the right hand side. With any luck you might get to the "certain stage" we were talking about. Then, reversing your argument, you should be able to go from the "certain stage" on to the right hand side and so complete the proof.

We now give examples of each of the four types mentioned above.

Example 1

The graph $y = 2 \sin\left(\frac{\pi}{2}x\right)$ intersects the x-axis at the point $A(a, 0)$ where a is the smallest positive value possible. Find the maximum area of $\triangle OAP$, where P is a point on the graph. Find Q, when the area of $\triangle OAQ$ is one.

Solution

First draw the graph.

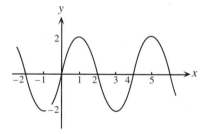

Where is A? Since a is the smallest positive value possible where $y = 2 \sin\left(\frac{\pi x}{2}\right)$ crosses the x-axis, a must equal 2. Hence A is $(2, 0)$.

Now where is P? We know that O and A are fixed. What can we say about P if $\triangle OAP$ has maximum area?

We know that the area of $\triangle OAP = \frac{1}{2}$ base $\times$ height. Since the base $OA = 2$, then the area of $\triangle OAP$ is just the height of the triangle. For $\triangle OAP$ to have maximum area, the distance of P from the x-axis must be as large as possible. This will happen at $x = 1, 3$ (who said $\triangle OAP$ had to be above the x-axis?), 5, 7, 9, ... At these values of x, $|y| = 2$. Hence the maximum area of $\triangle OAP = 2$.

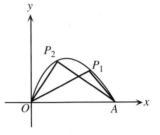

If the area of $\triangle OAQ$ is one, then Q is $(q, 1)$ or $(q, -1)$ (from the discussion above). So we have to solve $2 \sin \frac{\pi}{2} x = 1$ and $2 \sin \frac{\pi x}{2} = -1$.

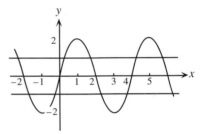

For the first equation, $\sin \frac{\pi x}{2} = \frac{1}{2}$. Now from Section 2 we know that

$\sin 30° = \sin \frac{\pi}{6} = \sin \frac{5\pi}{6} = \frac{1}{2}$. Further $\sin \left(\frac{\pi}{6} + 2n\pi \right) = \frac{1}{2}$ and $\sin \left(\frac{5\pi}{6} + 2n\pi \right) = \frac{1}{2}$.

Hence $\frac{\pi x}{2} = \frac{\pi}{6} + 2n\pi$ or $\frac{5\pi}{6} + 2n\pi$.

So $x = \frac{1}{3} + 4n$ or $\frac{5}{3} + 4n$, n an integer.

On the other hand, $\sin 210° = -\frac{1}{2}$ and $\sin 330° = -\frac{1}{2}$. Converting this to radians and repeating the steps above gives $x = \frac{7}{3} + 4n$ or $\frac{11}{3} + 4n$.

The points Q are therefore of the form $\left(\frac{1}{3} + 4n, 1 \right), \left(\frac{5}{3} + 4n, 1 \right), \left(\frac{7}{3} + 4n, -1 \right)$ and $\left(\frac{11}{3} + 4n, -1 \right)$.

Comment
You can see that more than one skill is often required in solving a problem. Even when we thought we were solving a graphical problem, we still had to find the solution of some trigonometric equations.

Example 2
Solve the equation $6\cos^2 A + 5\sin A = 2$, where $0 \le A \le 2\pi$.

Solution

The first thing to note here is that any solutions we find are to be restricted to lying between 0 and 2π, inclusive. So we are not going to end up with infinite sets of solutions as we did in Example 1.

The second thing to worry about is how on earth we are going to solve the equation at all! If the $\cos^2 A$ term had been $\sin^2 A$ we might have tried thinking of the equation as a quadratic in $\sin A$. With $\cos^2 A$ there, the thing looks like a mess. Ah, but wait!

We know that $\sin^2 A + \cos^2 A = 1$, so $\cos^2 A = 1 - \sin^2 A$. If we substitute for $\cos^2 A$, we will indeed get a quadratic in $\sin A$ that we might be able to solve after all!

$$6\cos^2 A + 5\sin A = 2.$$

Hence $6\left(1 - \sin^2 A\right) + 5\sin A = 2.$

Rearranging we get $6\sin^2 A - 5\sin A - 4 = 0$.

Does this factorise? If it doesn't we can always use good old $-\dfrac{b \pm \sqrt{b^2 - 4ac}}{2a}$. But let's leave that for an emergency. Think positively. Think factorisation.

After a bit of a struggle, we get $(3\sin A - 4)(2\sin A + 1) = 0$.

Hence $3\sin A - 4 = 0$ or $2\sin A + 1 = 0$, and $\sin A = \dfrac{4}{3}$ or $-\dfrac{1}{2}$.

How can $\sin A = \dfrac{4}{3}$? I don't remember seeing anything like that before! Of course not! The sine function has no value bigger than 1. So $\sin A = \dfrac{4}{3}$ has no solutions anywhere.

So $\sin A = -\dfrac{1}{2}$. This has two solutions. We can tell that from the graph. From what we have done before we see that $A = \pi + \dfrac{\pi}{6}$ or $2\pi - \dfrac{\pi}{6}$.

Hence $A = \dfrac{7\pi}{6}$ or $\dfrac{11\pi}{6}$.

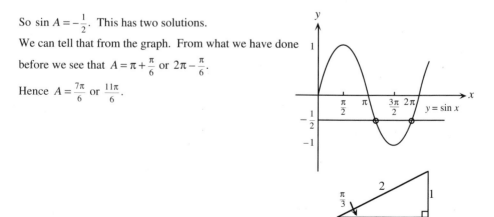

Comments

The first thing to notice here was the restriction on A. Then we had to struggle to change the equation into a quadratic in $\sin A$. Can we change the equation to a quadratic in $\cos A$? That's unlikely. There's no way I can think of to change $\sin A$ into something linear in $\cos A$.

It's always worth checking your answer just in case you've made a mistake. I'll leave it for you to do that.

Example 3

In the diagram, two trees at C and D are on the edge of a river whose width is being calculated. On an island in the river, stakes at A and B are driven into the ground 100 metres apart. Various angles are measured. It is found that $\angle ABD = 30°$, $\angle CAD = 150°$, $\angle ABC = 45°$ and $\angle BAD = 105°$. Calculate the distance CD, the width of the river.

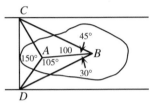

Solution

This is quite a complicated situation. With a bit of reflection we can see that
$\angle ADB = 180° - (105° + 30°) = 45°$, $\angle CAB = 360° - (150° + 105°) = 105°$ and
$\angle ACB = 180° - (105° + 45°) = 30°$.

So in $\triangle ABD$, we have all the angles and one side so we can find the other two sides using the sine rule.

Now we're trying to find CD. What do we know about $\triangle ACD$ or $\triangle BCD$? Can we use trigonometry to find CD in either of these triangles? In $\triangle ACD$ we can find AC and AD and we know $\angle CAD$. So we could use the cosine rule in $\triangle BCD$ to find CD.

That at least gives us a plan of attack - two plans actually, depending on whether we prefer to work with $\triangle ACD$ or $\triangle BCD$. I'll choose $\triangle ACD$ on your behalf. You can check using $\triangle BCD$. Let me summarise my steps.

Step 1: Find AC in $\triangle ABC$ using the sine rule.
Step 2: Find AD in $\triangle ABD$ using the sine rule.
Step 3: Find CD in $\triangle ACD$ using the cosine rule.

Does all of that make sense? It looks like a lot of work but I think it makes sense. Let's try it out.

Step 1: $\dfrac{AC}{\sin \angle ABC} = \dfrac{AB}{\sin \angle ACB}$

Then $AC = \dfrac{AB}{\sin \angle ACB} \cdot \sin \angle ABC$

$= \dfrac{100}{\sin 30°} \cdot \sin 45° = 100\sqrt{2}.$

I'll leave it like that just now. I'm too lazy to turn on my calculator.

Step 2: $\dfrac{AD}{\sin \angle ABD} = \dfrac{AB}{\sin \angle ADB}$

Then $AD = \dfrac{AB}{\sin \angle ADB} \cdot \sin \angle ABD$

$= \dfrac{100}{\sin 45°} \cdot \sin 30° = 50\sqrt{2}.$

Again I'll leave it in that form for now.

Step 3: $CD^2 = AC^2 + AD^2 - 2 \cdot AC \cdot AD \cos \angle CAD$

$= \left(100\sqrt{2}\right)^2 + \left(50\sqrt{2}\right)^2 - 2\left(100\sqrt{2}\right)\left(50\sqrt{2}\right)\cos 150°$

$= 20\,000 + 5000 - 20\,000 \cos 150°$

$= 25\,000 - 20\,000 \times \left(-\dfrac{\sqrt{3}}{2}\right)$

$\cong 42\,321.$

I must say I can only do the square root on my calculator. After pressing a button or two I get
$CD = \sqrt{42\,321} \cong 205.7$ metres, to one decimal.

Example 4

Prove that $\dfrac{\tan y - \tan x}{\tan y + \tan x} = \dfrac{\sin (y - x)}{\sin (y + x)}.$

Solution

With all identities it's a matter of taking the LHS and showing that it's equivalent to the RHS, or, if you are left handed, taking the RHS and showing it's equivalent to the LHS. But which way should you try first? That's up to you, but some identities do seem to want to have one side or the other expanded or somehow worked on.

In the above example, let's work on the LHS first. The reason I want to do this is because

$\tan y = \dfrac{\sin y}{\cos y}$ and I think that I can do myself some good by multiplying by cosines. Watch

me!

$$\text{LHS} = \frac{\tan y - \tan x}{\tan y + \tan x} = \frac{\dfrac{\sin y}{\cos y} - \dfrac{\sin x}{\cos x}}{\dfrac{\sin y}{\cos y} + \dfrac{\sin x}{\cos x}}$$

$$= \frac{\dfrac{\sin y \cos x - \sin x \cos y}{\cos x \cos y}}{\dfrac{\sin y \cos x + \sin x \cos y}{\cos x \cos y}} = \frac{\sin y \cos x - \sin x \cos y}{\sin y \cos x + \sin x \cos y}.$$

How about that! Both the numerator and the denominator are formulas I recognize. In fact,

$$\text{LHS} = \frac{\sin (y - x)}{\sin (y + x)}$$

$$= \text{RHS}.$$

There; I did it.

But of course the calculations can be done in reverse. So I could have started out with the RHS.

$$\text{RHS} = \frac{\sin (y - x)}{\sin (y + x)}$$

$$= \frac{\sin y \cos x - \cos y \sin x}{\sin y \cos x + \cos y \sin x}$$

$$= \frac{\dfrac{\sin y \cos x - \cos y \sin x}{\cos y \cos x}}{\dfrac{\sin y \cos x + \cos y \sin x}{\cos y \cos x}}$$

(Admittedly this step may have required divine intervention, but...)

$$= \frac{\dfrac{\sin y}{\cos y} - \dfrac{\sin x}{\cos x}}{\dfrac{\sin y}{\cos y} + \dfrac{\sin x}{\cos x}}$$

$$= \frac{\tan y - \tan x}{\tan y + \tan x}$$

$$= \text{LHS}.$$

Bingo!

Example 5

Prove the identity

$$\left(\sin^4 A + \cos^4 A\right)\left(\tan A + \cot A\right)^2 = \tan^2 A + \cot^2 A.$$

Solution

This worries me. It's not the $\cot A$. I know that's $\dfrac{1}{\tan A}$. The thing that disturbs me at first sight is that the LHS looks like something to the power 6 (the fourth power in the first bracket combined with the second bracket), while the RHS looks like a power of 2!

Well, I suppose they know what they're doing, so I'll hop straight in. And I think that the LHS looks more like something that can be played with than the RHS, so I'll start that way.

$$\text{LHS} = \left(\sin^4 A + \cos^4 A\right)\left(\tan A + \cot A\right)^2$$

$$= \left(\sin^4 A + \cos^4 A\right)\left(\frac{\sin A}{\cos A} + \frac{\cos A}{\sin A}\right)^2$$

$$= \left(\sin^4 A + \cos^4 A\right)\left(\frac{\sin^2 A + \cos^2 A}{\sin A \cos A}\right)^2$$

$$= \frac{\sin^4 A + \cos^4 A}{\sin^2 A \cos^2 A}$$

$$= \frac{\sin^2 A}{\cos^2 A} + \frac{\cos^2 A}{\sin^2 A}$$

$$= \tan^2 A + \cot^2 A$$

$$= \text{RHS}.$$

Wow! A thing that looked as though it might be tremendously complicated turned out to be quite within reach. It certainly is evidence of the old maxim "Everything looks hard until you try it".

6.4   *Trigonometric Applications*

Things that oscillate have the potential to be trigonometric. Unfortunately, in real life things are never perfect, since gravity, friction, and so on always distort. But we can give you a feel for some of the applications of this terrific topic.

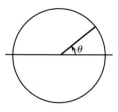

Figure 7

Take a wheel of radius R that has a fixed centre and is moving with a constant angular speed. This means that the angle θ in Figure 7 that the wheel has turned through at any time is some constant multiple of t, the time measured in some units, seconds say. So $\theta = kt$. If the wheel makes one revolution in 4 secs. then when $\theta = 2\pi$, $t = 4$ so $2\pi = 4k$, or $k = \frac{\pi}{2}$. This gives $\theta = \frac{\pi}{2}t$.

Now let a piece of paper move constantly past the wheel. If we put a pen on the rim of the wheel, what shape would the pen draw? (See Figure 8(a).)

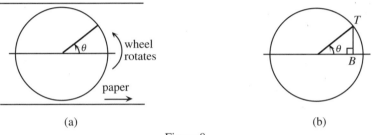

(a)   (b)

Figure 8

I'll leave it for you to speculate, and possibly to experiment. Does the speed with which the paper moves have any impact on the resulting curve?

Now suppose we put a pen on a pendulum. A pendulum is the most regular of things. If it is moving with a period of 4 seconds does the pen on the pendulum draw a sinusoidal curve? Well, suppose the length of the pendulum is 1 and the pendulum's maximum swing is an angle of α. From the right-angled triangle OAB I can see that $x = 1\sin\theta$. So things look good for another sine curve, especially when we realise that θ can be as large as α. But things are never as simple as these seem. Again, I'll leave it for you to ponder.

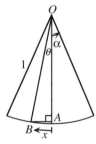

Figure 9

Another regular phenomenon of nature is tides. They ebb and flow periodically in such a way that they may appear to be simple sine curves. In fact they are not as simple as you might think. Get hold of some tables of tides and try to model them using the sine function.

The big problem with tides is that they vary in amplitude. Some times they are higher than at other times. What has this got to do with the moon? Has it got anything to do with the Sun? How can we predict tides? Is there a relatively simple formula?

All this has, of course, been worked out. You might like to chase it up but have a crack at it for yourself first.

Having discovered that two of the most natural periodic objects are not quite sines you might think that there are not many uses for them. Well, perhaps not by themselves but put a lot of them together and quite complicated and periodic behaviour can be modelled. However, this gets us into things called Fourier Series, and they're a long way off from the problems that you are about to face.

Problems

If you get stuck on a problem, there are some hints beginning on page 116.

1. Find all values of x that satisfy the equation $2 \sin^2 x - 3 \sin x - 2 = 0$ for $-\pi \le x \le \pi$.

2. Determine all values of θ between 0 and π radians such that $6 \cos^2 \theta - \sin \theta = 4$.

3. If $\cos 2\theta = -\frac{7}{9}$ and $0 < \theta < \frac{\pi}{2}$, find $\cos \theta$.

4. Prove that $\tan \theta + \cot \theta = \dfrac{2}{\sin(2\theta)}$, $0 < \theta < \frac{\pi}{2}$.

5. Prove the identity: $1 - \dfrac{\sin^2 \theta}{1 + \cot \theta} - \dfrac{\cos^2 \theta}{1 + \tan \theta} = \dfrac{\sin(2\theta)}{2}$.

6. Prove that $1 + \tan(2x) \tan x = \sec(2x)$.

7. Prove the identity $\dfrac{\sin(4x)}{1 - \cos(4x)} = \cot x - \frac{1}{2} \csc x \sec x$.

8. (a) If $0° < A < 90°$, and $\sin A = 0.1$, find the value of $\log_{10}(\tan A) + \log_{10}(\cos A)$.

    (b) If $\sin 2t = 0$, find the number of possible values of $\sin t$.

    (c) Find all the roots of the equation $\sin^2 \theta = 1 - \cos \theta$, for $0 \le \theta \le 2\pi$.

9. What is the smallest positive value of x, in degrees, for which $\cos(9x) = \sin(9x)$?

10. If $2 \sin(2\theta) + 1 = 0$, find the smallest positive value of θ (in degrees).

11. In the diagram, arc AB is 5π units and the angle at the centre is $150°$. Find the length of chord AB, correct to one decimal place.

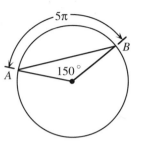

12. In triangle ABC, $\sin B = \frac{3}{5}$ and $\sin C = \frac{1}{4}$. Determine the ratio $AB:BC$.

13. A vertical flagpole CD stands on a level plane and has height h. Observations are taken in the plane at points A and B which lie in a straight line with the foot D of the pole. If AB is m units, and the angles of elevation of C from A and B are α and β respectively, determine h in terms of α, β, and m.

14. For $0 \le \theta \le \frac{\pi}{2}$, sketch the graphs of $y = \cos 4\theta$ and $y = \sin 3\theta$ on the same set of axes.

   How many solutions does the equation $\cos 4\theta = \sin 3\theta$ have for $0 \le \theta \le \frac{\pi}{2}$?

15. The graph of the equation $y = a \sin kx$ is shown in the diagram, and the point $\left(\frac{3\pi}{4}, -2\right)$ is the minimun point indicated. The line $y = 1$ intersects the graph at point D. What are the coordinates of D?

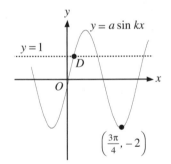

16. Graph $y = \sin \theta$ for $0 \le \theta \le 2\pi$.
   (i)   On the same axes, sketch the graphs of $y = \sin \theta$ and $y = |\sin \theta|$, $0 \le \theta \le 2\pi$.
   (ii) On a second set of axes, sketch the graph $f(0) = \sin \theta + |\sin \theta|$, $0 \le \theta \le 2\pi$.
   (iii) Determine all values of θ for which $f(\theta) = 0$, $0 \le \theta \le 2\pi$.

17. Given that $\sin^2(2x) - \sin^2 x = \sin(2x) \sin x$, where $0 \le x \le \frac{\pi}{2}$, determine all possible values of $\sin x$.

18. For what values of θ, $-\frac{\pi}{2} \le \theta \le \frac{\pi}{2}$, does the equation $x^2 + (2 \sin \theta)x + \cos(2\theta) = 0$ have real roots? If you use a calculator, express your answer correct to two decimal places.

19. Prove there are no real values of x such that $2 \sin x = x^2 - 4x + 6$.

20. In the diagram, a box in the shape of a cube with side 1.2 m is sitting on a hand cart 1 m from the front end, A, of the cart platform. The platform AB is parallel to the floor. The wheels on the cart have radii 0.4 m. The back end of the platform is lifted so that point B is rotated $15°$ about the point A. What is the minimum height of a doorway through which the cart can pass? Give your answer correct to one decimal place. You may ignore the thickness of the platform and assume the box does not slip when the cart is lifted.

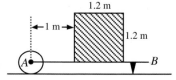

21. A rectangle is inscribed between the graphs of $y = 3 \sin\left(\frac{x}{2}\right)$ and $y = 3 \cos\left(\frac{x}{2}\right)$, and below the x-axis, as shown. If AB is $\frac{\pi}{3}$, what is the area of the rectangle?

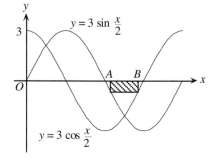

Chapter 7   Calculus

7.1   The Method of Exhaustion

Calculus was actually the answer to a mathematician's prayer. Well, to a seventeenth century mathematician's prayer. In 1659, the Dutch mathematician Huygens was tearing his hair out about the current development of mathematics

> "Mathematicians will never have enough time to read all the discoveries in Geometry (a quantity which is increasing from day to day and seems likely in this scientific age to develop to enormous proportions) if they continue to be presented in a rigorous form according to the manner of the ancients."

The problem was not so much the **results** that were being produced at the time, though there were certainly plenty of new developments. Rather it was the long and subtle **arguments** that were required to produce the latest results. Basically mathematicians had got into a rut, technique-wise, with a process called the **method of exhaustion**.

Now this method of exhaustion supposedly goes back to a Greek mathematician by the name of Eudoxus who lived between about 400 and 347 B.C. Some of his work can be found in Euclid's famous geometry book, The Elements. The basic idea of the method can be seen from the following proof that the area of a circle is proportional to its radius.

One takes successively closer approximations in an attempt to reach a conclusion. For example, in approximating the area of a circle, it is clear that one could put similar polygons inside and outside the circle and that the circle area must lie between the areas of these figures. If the polygons are squares, the outside polygon has area $4r^2$ while the inner polygon has area $2r^2$, so if the circle area is A, we know that $2r^2 < A < 4r^2$.

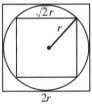

Figure 1

If the polygons are hexagons, the outside polygon has area

$$6\left[\frac{1}{2}\cdot\frac{2r}{\sqrt{3}}\cdot r\right] = 2\sqrt{3}r^2, \text{ which is approximately } 3.464r^2,$$

while the inner polygon has area $6\left[\frac{1}{2}r\cdot\frac{\sqrt{3}}{2}r\right] = \frac{3\sqrt{3}}{2}r^2$,

which is approximately $2.598r^2$, so now we know that

$2.598r^2 < A < 3.464r^2$.

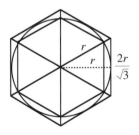

Figure 2

Now we have a better approximation. If we repeat the process using 12-sided polygons we get a better approximation still, and continuing this process we get closer and closer to a true value.

Now the above argument is not too bad. But some of these method of exhaustion proofs were extremely intricate. Consequently it was taking Huygens more time than he had to spare, to keep up with the research literature of his day.

Part of the problem was that mathematicians were skirting the implicit problems of an infinite sequence of steps and consequential limit processes. This was being done by using an appropriate finite number of steps. In the argument above, we only needed to to as far as a polygon which was suitably close in area to the circle.

So it was calculus to the rescue. The very name calculus has something to do with calculations. What calculus did, and did extremely well, was to enable results which had hitherto required the method of exhaustion, to be produced very efficiently. A whole range of tangents and maxima and minima for algebraic curves could be found with little more than the knowledge of the derivative process.

Having extolled the power of calculus over the methods existing at the time, you would think that it would have been welcomed with open arms. Surprisingly, this wasn't the case.

When Newton sent off his two founding works, De Analysis and De Methodis Serierum et Fluxionum to the Royal Society and the Cambridge University Press, they were rejected! As a result the first paper that was published on calculus was Leibniz production of 1684. This sparked a bitter row between the Newton and Leibniz camps over who had thought of it first.

The situation is now clear. It is certainly true that Newton was first. However it is also clear that Leibniz produced the notation, $\dfrac{dy}{dx}$, that we use for derivatives and the sign, $\int$, that we use for integration.

From the start, then, there were two sides to the calculus, differentiation and integration. Differentiation was good for finding tangents, maxima and minima, and so on. It was also good for finding speed and acceleration and expressing these in terms of derivatives. Differentiation was also useful in producing differential equations - equations involving derivatives. These equations were particularly valuable in expressing mechanical laws in terms of algebraic expressions.

On the other hand, integration was extremely useful when it came to finding areas and volumes. Leibniz also showed that integration is the inverse operation of differentiation. As such, integration can theoreticaly "undo" differentiation. So integration can be used to solve differential equations. Well, sometimes it can. The surprising thing is that while we can differentiate almost everything reasonable, even fairly innocuous looking things often cannot be integrated.

Newton had the answer to this. All he did was to express everything in terms of infinite series and then integrate them term by term as a collection of powers of x. But his method has its limitations, so it happens that many of the useful things one might want to integrate in practice can't be done. It's here that computer software systems like Maple become extremely useful.

7.2   *Differentiation*

If you wanted to find the equation of a tangent to a curve, how would you do it? First of all you might want to know what a tangent is. It's simply a line which touches a curve at a point (although it may, further on, cut the curve at a second point).

Look at the four parallel lines in Figure 3. The first hits the curve, $y = f(x)$ at two points A_1 and B_1. The second hits the curve at two points A_2 and B_2. But A_2 and B_2 are closer together then A_1 and B_1. As we move the parallel line 2 toward the parallel line 3, A_2 and B_2 move closer together until they meet at the single point C. As line 3 moves to line 4, there are no points of intersection with $y = f(x)$. We say that line 3 is the **tangent** to the curve $y = f(x)$ at the point C.

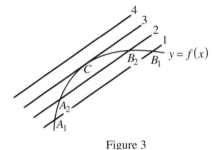

Figure 3

Now if we had to find the gradient, or slope, of $y = x^2$ at $x = 1$, how could we do it? One way would be to draw $y = x^2$ very carefully on graph paper, then stick a ruler up against the point $(1,1)$. We could probably then draw the tangent in. Then we could work out the gradient of the straight line by finding the quotient of the difference between two of its y-values and the difference between corresponding x-values. But that's not likely to be too accurate. My guess is that any two times you did that, you'd get two different answers. So how could you sneak up on it?

Well suppose we didn't try for perfection first up. Just draw any old straight line through the point $P(1,1)$. (See Figure 4). Well perhaps not **any** old straight line.

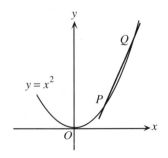

Figure 4

Let's make sure the line hits $y = x^2$ at some point Q. It's pretty obvious that the gradient of the line PQ is not the gradient of $y = x^2$ at P. On the other hand, it's not too far off. And we can get a closer value by rotating the line PQ so that it hits $y = x^2$ at a point nearer to P than Q. (See Q_1 in Figure 5).

Figure 5

Surely as we rotate PQ_1, we can get a point Q_2 on $y = x^2$ so that PQ_2 is an even better approximation to the tangent at P.

Exercises

1. Try to formalise the approximation process. If Q is some point close to P, what is the gradient of PQ? How does this help you find the gradient of $y = x^2$ at P? Try using Q successively having x-values 2, 1.5, 1.2, 1.1, 1.05. Can you guess what the tangent gradient is?

2. Repeat the last exercise in an effort to find the gradient of $y = x^2$ at $R(3, 9)$, using x-values you choose for Q.

3. What is the gradient of $y = x^2$ at the point $S(a, a^2)$?

4. How many tangents are there from the point $A(a, b)$ to the parabola $y = x^2$?

That Exercise 4 has been worrying me. Doesn't the answer depend to some extent on where the point $P(a, b)$ is? If A is in certain parts of the plane, there are no tangents from it to the parabola $y = x^2$. On the other hand, if A is in certain other parts, there are **two** tangents. You can see this by looking at Figure 6.

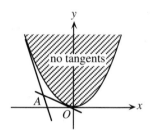

Figure 6

Exercises

5. Is it true that there must be either 0 or 2 tangents through (a, b)?

6. How many tangents can be drawn from (a, b) to the curve $y = x^3$? Are there a different number of tangents depending on what part of the plane (a, b) belongs to?

We can actually formalise that business of the gradient of the line PQ from Figure 4. We know that $P(1, 1)$ is on $y = x^2$. Let Q be another point on $y = x^2$ having x-coordinate $1 + h$. Its y-coordinate will then be $(1 + h)^2$.

Finding the gradient of the line PQ is easy. It's just

$$\frac{y_2 - y_1}{x_2 - x_1} = \frac{(1 + h)^2 - 1}{(1 + h) - 1}.$$

This simplifies to give a gradient of

$$\frac{h^2 + 2h}{h} = h + 2.$$

But remember, the gradient of the curve at P is just the gradient of PQ as Q gets closer and closer to P. This is the same as letting h get closer and closer to zero.

As h approaches 0, $h + 2$ approaches 2. The gradient at P is just 2!

That was pretty easy. Why did Newton and Leibniz make all that fuss about discovering calculus?

Exercises

7.   Find the gradient of the curve $y = x^2$ at $x = 3$.
8.   Find the gradient of the curve $y = x^3 - 2x$ at $x = 2$.
9.   Find the gradients of all the curves at all the points you haven't managed so far.
10.   Find the gradient of $y = f(x)$ at the point $(a, f(a))$. (We write the general gradient as

either $\dfrac{dy}{dx}$ or $f'(x)$).

7.3   Mathematical Skills

As is usual I list below all the calculus skills that I think you might need to do the problems of this chapter. If you don't know them I suggest that you talk to your teacher about getting a book from which you can learn them. In the past I've reminded you that any mathematical skill we used in earlier chapters might be needed again here. You have been warned!

And just to show how kind we can be, we have only produced questions that need differentiation. For now you can forget about integration.

Basic Derivatives

If $y = x^n$, then $\dfrac{dy}{dx} = nx^{n-1}$ (this is true for any real value of n).

If $y = c$, where c is a constant, then $\dfrac{dy}{dx} = 0$.

If $y = \sin x$, then $\dfrac{dy}{dx} = \cos x$.

If $y = \cos x$, then $\dfrac{dy}{dx} = -\sin x$.

If $y = \tan x$, then $\dfrac{dy}{dx} = \sec^2 x$.

If $y = \ln x$, where $x > 0$, then $\dfrac{dy}{dx} = \dfrac{1}{x}$.

If $y = e^x$, then $\dfrac{dy}{dx} = e^x$.

Rules for Differentiation

Product Rule: If $y = f(x) \cdot g(x)$, then $\dfrac{dy}{dx} = f(x)\dfrac{dg}{dx} + \dfrac{df}{dx}g(x)$.

Quotient Rule: If $y = \dfrac{f(x)}{g(x)}$, then $\dfrac{dy}{dx} = \dfrac{g(x)\dfrac{df}{dx} - f(x)\dfrac{dg}{dx}}{g^2(x)}$.

Chain Rule: If $y = f(g(x))$, then $\dfrac{dy}{dx} = \dfrac{df}{dg} \cdot \dfrac{dg}{dx}$.

For example, if u is a function of x, $\dfrac{d}{dx}u^m = mu^{m-1}\dfrac{du}{dx}$

and $\dfrac{d}{dx}x^n y^m = nx^{n-1}y^m + mx^n y^{m-1}\dfrac{dy}{dx}$.

Turning Points

The curve $y = f(x)$ has **turning points** where $\dfrac{dy}{dx} = 0$. These points may be local maxima or local minima depending on the shape of the graph. In Figure 7, we show local maxima at points P_1 and P_2, while local minima are shown at points R_1 and R_2.

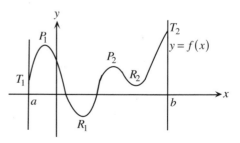

Figure 7

Sometimes the domain (or values of x) of a function may be restricted, perhaps because of some physical constraint. This may cause extreme values (either maxima or minima) to occur at endpoints of the domain. In Figure 7, T_1 and T_2 are endpoints of the curve. The point T_2 is an absolute maximum in this case. The point T_1 is neither a minimum nor a maximum point.

Tests for Extreme Points

First Derivative Test

If the derivative to the left of a point where $\dfrac{dy}{dx} = 0$ is negative and to the right is positive, then the turning point is a maximum point.
If the derivative is positive to the left of the point and negative to the right, the turning point is a minimum.

maximum

maximum

Caution: There are cases for which the above does not apply.

For example, in the diagram at the right, $\dfrac{dy}{dx}$ does not exist at P, but there is a local maximum at P. We won't include any such cases in the problems in this book.

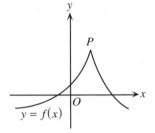

Second Derivative Test

If $\dfrac{d^2y}{dx^2}$ (the derivative of $\dfrac{dy}{dx}$) is negative at a turning point; then the turning point is a local maximum.

If $\dfrac{d^2y}{dx^2}$ is positive at a turning point, then the turning point is a local minimum.

$$\frac{d^2y}{dx^2} < 0$$

maximum

$$\frac{d^2y}{dx^2} > 0$$

minimum

More On $\dfrac{d^2y}{dx^2}$

If $\dfrac{d^2y}{dx^2}$ is negative in an interval, then the curve is concave down in that interval. If $\dfrac{d^2y}{dx^2}$ is positive in an interval, then the curve is concave up in that interval.

$$\frac{d^2y}{dx^2} < 0$$

concave down

$$\frac{d^2y}{dx^2} > 0$$

concave up

If $\dfrac{d^2y}{dx^2} = 0$ at a point P on a curve and if the curve is concave down at one side of P and concave up at the other side, then P is called a point of inflection. In short, a point of inflection is a point at which concavity changes.

Points of inflection also occur under other circumstances. You might try finding the point of inflection for the curve whose equation is $y = x^{\frac{1}{3}}$.

If is also possible for both first and second derivatives to be zero at a point of inflection. You might check this at the point $(2, 1)$ on the curve defined by $f(x) = (x - 2)^3 + 1$.

It is not sufficient to say that a point of inflection occurs where $\dfrac{d^2y}{dx^2} = 0$. For example, $f(x) = x^4 + 1$ has no points of inflection and yet $\dfrac{d^2y}{dx^2} = 0$ when $x = 0$.

7.4   *Problem Solving Skills*

In a lot of calculus problems it is important to draw a diagram. Diagrams are very useful to give you a feel of what is going on, what the important ideas are, and so on. A picture is very useful when a tangent has to be found or when shadows are moving around the place.

The other skill, which is possibly more important here than in some other types of problems, is reading the question. Many of the calculus word problems are quite complicated and it's a good idea to read them very varefully. I'd actually suggest that you read most problems twice before you even start on a diagram, and then once more when you're happy with the diagram. It usually pays to read the problem again sometime during your working and yet again at the end. Some problems have two steps where you first have to find something and then do something with what you have found. For these questions a quick look at the problem half way through is always worth the time spent.

I'll now do a couple of problems to get you warmed up for the hazards ahead. You may have seen the first question somewhere before.

Problem 1

How many tangents are there from the point (a, b) to the parabola $y = x^2$?

Comments

First things first. Draw a diagram. So here goes Figure 8. It occurs to me that a tangent from (a, b) to the curve might be at (c, c^2). Note that I use (c, c^2) for a point on the curve, rather than using (c, d) which introduces two variables. Since $y = x^2$, it's easy to see that $d = c^2$.

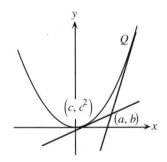

Figure 8

Solution

If the line is a tangent at (c, c^2), then I can find its gradient (or slope) in two ways. First, the gradient of the line between (a, b) and (c, c^2) is

$$m = \frac{c^2 - b}{c - a}.$$

The other way is by calculus. Since $y = x^2$, $\frac{dy}{dx} = 2x$. At the point (c, c^2), the gradient is $2c$.

Hence

$$2c = \frac{c^2 - b}{c - a}.$$

Tidying up I get

$$2c(c-a)=c^2-b$$

or $$c^2-2ac+b=0$$

and then $$c=\frac{2a\pm\sqrt{4a^2-4b}}{2}$$

$$=a\pm\sqrt{a^2-b}.$$

So I get two values of c where the tangent from (a,b) meets the curve at $\left(c,c^2\right)$. The tangents meet the curve at $a+\sqrt{a^2-b}$ and $a-\sqrt{a^2-b}$.

Hmm! That's all very well and good but sometimes I'm sure you can't get **one** tangent from (a,b) let alone **two**! But I always seem to get **two**!

Ah, of course! Remember the discriminant is a^2-b! I need $a^2\geq b$ or else the square root doesn't give me a real number. If $a^2>b$, I get two tangent values (like I found above.) If $a^2=b$, I just get $c=a$. If $a^2<b$, then there's no tangent at all.

A little bit of work shows that if $a^2>b$, then the point (a,b) is **below** the parabola (just as I've shown in Figure 8). Naturally if $a^2=b$, then $(a,b)=\left(a,a^2\right)$ is already **on** the parabola. That's why there's only **one** tangent in that case.

Finally if $a^2<b$, then (a,b) is above the parabola. You can't get a tangent at all from there to the curve.

It's interesting to note that I could have done the whole thing without calculus. I could find the equation of the line through (a,b) and $\left(c,c^2\right)$ and impose the condition for tangency that the roots of the resulting quadratic equation must be equal. That looks really messy! It would probably be simpler to use the family of lines through (a,b) and impose tangency conditions. You might be interested in trying that.

Problem 2
For a pole erected on the equator, how fast is the length of its shadow moving at time t?

Comment
I wonder why this pole is erected at the equator? Maybe you want to think about that.

Solution

And the diagram is... (see Figure 9)

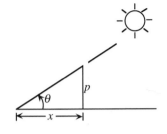

Figure 9

I'll probably need the height of the pole - call it p. But what must I find? How fast the shadow is moving. Let x be the distance of the end of the shadow from the foot of the pole. What I'm after is $\dfrac{dx}{dt}$, the speed of the shadow's tip.

So what? How can I find $\dfrac{dx}{dt}$? $\dfrac{dx}{dt} = \dfrac{dx}{d\theta} \cdot \dfrac{d\theta}{dt}$? What's the use of that? I suppose if I could find $\dfrac{dx}{d\theta}$ and $\dfrac{d\theta}{dt}$, I'd be OK. Of course, finding those quantities may be impossible. What else do I know? The sun! The sun is moving round the Earth! Well, relatively speaking. It goes round once in 24 hours and it's apparent angular speed is always the same. That means $\theta = kt$. When $t = 24$, $\theta = 2\pi$, so $2\pi = 24k$. And $k = \dfrac{\pi}{12}$. Now $\theta = \dfrac{\pi}{12}t$, so $\dfrac{d\theta}{dt} = \dfrac{\pi}{12}$.

One derivative down and one to go. How to get $\dfrac{dx}{d\theta}$? Perhaps x and θ are linked somehow.

Aha, the triangle with the flagpole! $\dfrac{p}{x} = \tan \theta$. So $x = \dfrac{p}{\tan \theta} = \dfrac{p \cos \theta}{\sin \theta}$. Now I can find $\dfrac{dx}{d\theta}$ using the quotient rule!

$$\frac{dx}{d\theta} = p\left[\frac{\sin \theta(-\sin \theta) - \cos \theta(\cos \theta)}{\sin^2 \theta}\right]$$

$$= p\left[\frac{-\sin^2 \theta - \cos^2 \theta}{\sin^2 \theta}\right]$$

$$= \frac{-p}{\sin^2 \theta}.$$

Putting all of that together I get

$$\frac{dx}{dt} = \frac{dx}{d\theta} \cdot \frac{d\theta}{dt} = \frac{-\pi p}{12 \sin^2 \theta}.$$

Comment

Why the minus sign, I wonder? I guess I've taken a Southern Hemisphere perspective, sorry about that, and the sun in Figure 9 is counter-clockwise. Until the sun gets directly over the flagpole the shadow is getting smaller and the speed is going from left to right. Since x is measured from the front of the flagpole it is moving in the negative direction of x. Its speed is therefore negative.

Hang on though. There's another problem. I seem suddenly to have subscribed to a flat Earth. Can I do the problem with the Earth as a sphere? You might like to address that problem yourself. The difficulty is that we have to use the pole's length (a few metres) and the earth's radius (a good many kilometres), and this makes the calculations very laborious.

Problems

If you get stuck on a problem, there are some hints beginning on page 116.

1.   Determine the equation of the tangent line to the curve whose equation is $y = \sqrt{x^2 + 3}$ at the point where $x = 1$.

2.   Determine the coordinates of the two points on the curve having equation
     $y = 2x^3 - 8x + 40$ at which the tangents to the curve have slope -2, and determine the equations of the tangents at these points.

3.   Determine the equation of the tangent to the parabola $y^2 = 8x$ that is parallel to the line $y = 4x + 5$.

4.   For the function with equation $y = (x-1)^2(4-x)$, determine the equation of the tangent line which has maximum slope.

5.   Determine the area of the triangle whose vertices are the local extreme points of the curve with equation $y = x^4 + 4x^3 - 8x^2$.

6.   A street lamp whose light is 5 metres from the ground is 6 metres from a vertical brick wall. A person, 2 metres tall, walks at right angles away from the wall directly towards the street lamp at a speed of 1.2 metres per second. At what speed is the shadow of the top of the person's head descending down the wall when the person is 1.5 metres from the wall?

7. Let C be a point on the positive x-axis and D be a point on the positive y-axis such that line CD is tangent to the curve with equation $y = \dfrac{8}{x}$, $x > 0$ at any point P, as shown in the diagram. Prove that P is the midpoint of segment CD.

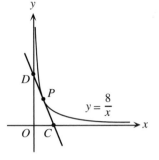

8. The graph of a function $y = f(x)$ has the properties:
   (i) vertical asymptotes $x = -1$ and $x = 4$
   (ii) a horizontal asymptote $y = 2$
   (iii) its only local maximum at the point $(1, 2)$ and its local minimum at the point $(2, 0)$.

   The function has the properies:
   (i) $f'(x) < 0$ for $x > 4$
   (ii) $f''(x) < 0$ for $x < -1$
   (iii) $f(x) = 0$ only for $x = -2$, $x = 0$, $x = 2$.

   Using this information, sketch the graph of $y = f(x)$.

9. Given that $\ln y = \dfrac{8}{x} + 4 \ln x - 3$, where $x, y > 0$, find

   (i) all local extrema
   (ii) the equation of the tangent at the point where $x = 1$.

10. P is any point on the curve with equation $y = x^3$. The tangent at P meets the curve again at Q. Prove that the slope of the curve at Q is four times the slope at P.

11. A window frame is to be manufactured as shown so that the bottom section $ABCD$ is three sides of a rectangle and the top section AED is a semicircular arc. If the cost of the semicircular component is $20 per metre and the cost of the rectangle components is $8 per metre, find the value of the width BC so that a frame enclosing a window of total area 16 m^2 has minimum cost.

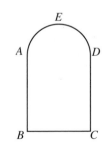

12. Consider the circles C_1, with centre $(x, 0)$ and passing through $(1, 1)$, and C_2, with centre $(x, 0)$ and passing through $(0, 1)$, where $x \geq 0$.

13. In triangle ABC, sides AB and AC have fixed lengths c and b respectively, with $c > b$, and BC has variable length a. Also, θ is the measure of $\angle CAB$ and h is the length of the altitude from A to BC.

   (a) State, without proof: (i) $\lim\limits_{\theta \to \pi} a$ and   (ii) $\lim\limits_{\theta \to 0} a$.

   (b) Prove that $\dfrac{da}{d\theta} = h$.

14. For the function defined by $f(x) = (4 - x)e^x$ find
   (i) x- and y-intercepts
   (ii)   local maxima
   (iii) points of inflection.
   Sketch the graph of $f(x)$ using the points obtained above and also the points where $x = -2, -4$, and -6. Convince yourself that the x-axis is an asymptote.

15. A man 2 metres tall walks along the edge of a straight road 10 metres wide. On the other edge of the road stands a streetlight 8 metres high. If the man walks at $\dfrac{3}{2}$ metres per second, how fast is his shadow lengthening when he is 10 metres past the point directly opposite the light?

16. A man is standing at a point A on the edge of a circular swimming pool of diameter 50 metres. He wishes to get to a point B diametrically opposite. He can run at 4 m/sec and swim at 2 m/sec. He runs around the edge of the pool to a point C, then swims directly from C to B. Where should C be chosen to minimize the total time taken to get from A to B? Assume no time is lost in diving into the water.

17. A billboard 6 m tall is located on top of a building with its lower edge 18 m above the level of a viewers eye. How far from a point directly below the sign should a viewer stand to maximize the angle θ between the lines of sight of the top and bottom of the billboard?

Chapter 8   *Counting Problems*

8.1   *Pascal's Triangle*

You may have seen the very famous triangle of
numbers that I've started to write out in Figure 1.
The dots are just to show that the numbers keep on
going. The triangle is called **Pascal's Triangle**.

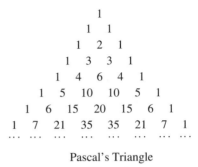

Pascal's Triangle
Figure 1

Exercises

1. Who was Pascal? Why was the triangle named after him? When was the triangle first seen?
2. Write down the next two rows of Pascal's Triangle.
3. What is the pattern that allows us to get the next number in the Triangle?

At the baseball park you can usually buy hot dogs, coke and French fries. How many ways can you choose two different things from this "menu"?

One way of going about this is to make some sort of systematic list. Let *h* stand for hot dog, *c* for coke and *f* for French fries. Then you should be able to get, in alphabetical order,

$$cf; \quad ch; \quad fh.$$

Only three, that's not much. Suppose I try to check it another way. Surely there are three possible ways to choose the first item. After that you've got a choice of 2 ways (three less the one I've already chosen) to get the second item. That means that there are $3 \times 2 = 6$ ways altogether.

Hmmm! Something fishy here. I get 3 by going the list route and 6 by doing some fancy counting. Which is right and why? (Or are they both wrong?)

Suppose I go back to that list again and bear in mind the counting method as I go. How many ways can I list the first item? Three ways, since any one of *c*, *f*, or *h* can be chosen first.

Then how many ways can I list the second item? Two ways since I've already chosen, c, f or h. So there must be six possible menus. Let me list them all.

c first	:	cf, ch
f first	:	fc, fh
h first	:	hc, hf

There are the six after all, if the order of choosing counts, but only three if order doesn't count.

Exercises
4.   Where did the "menu" count go wrong? Why?
5.   Suppose hamburgers were available too. How many ways can you have a meal with **two** items off of the menu?
6.   Suppose you wanted *three* items. How many ways could you buy them?

Of course, as you all know, any normal self-respecting baseball park will have n things on the menu. Equally well, you know that every red-blooded baseball fan will want to eat r items off the menu and certainly the order will not be important. So how many different ways can those r items be chosen. Naturally the answer is $\binom{n}{r}$. This peculiar symbol is pronounced "n choose r" because it tells us how to choose r things from set of n different things.

Now there are n ways of choosing the first item, $n-1$ the second, $n-2$ the third up to $n-r+1$ for the rth item. That's beginning to look like a count of $n(n-1)(n-2)...(n-r+1)$ until you realise that this way you produce an ordered count. Clearly you have to divide this by $r(r-1)...3.2.1$. Well no, maybe it's not clear. But you see that if you had the r things listed, you could list them in $r(r-1)(1-2)...3.2.1$ ways. Let me write that as $r!$ (pronounced r factorial) for short. So when we were doing the $n(n-1)(n-2)...(n-r+1)$ count we must have counted each particular r-sized set $r!$ times. In the coke, fries and hot dog case that'd be $2!$ times. And in our earlier list $\{c, f\}$ is counted twice, once as cf and the other time as fc. In fact the same thing happened to $\{c, h\}$ and $\{f, h\}$. Then my r item count must be

$$\binom{n}{r} = \frac{n(n-1)(n-2)...(n-r+1)}{r!}.$$

I can rewrite this a bit.

$$\binom{n}{r} = \frac{n(n-1)(n-2)...(n-r+1)}{r!}$$

$$= \frac{n(n-1)(n-2)...(n-r+1)}{r!} \cdot \frac{(n-r)(n-r-1)...3.2.1}{(n-r)(n-r-1)...3.2.1}$$

$$= \frac{n!}{r!(n-r)!}.$$

Which form is preferred? Well, it depends on what you're doing. If you wish to evaluate $\binom{8}{3}$,

then $\binom{8}{3} = \dfrac{8(7)(6)}{3(2)(1)} = 56$ is easiest. There are, however, situations in which the second form is more useful.

Exercises

7. Write out the values of the following:

   (i) $\binom{3}{2}$;   (ii) $\binom{4}{2}$;   (iii) $\binom{10}{6}$.

8. Find n and r to solve the following equations:

   (i) $\binom{n}{r} = 56$;   (ii) $\binom{n}{r} = 126$;   (iii) $\binom{n}{r} = 462$.

9. Find an equation linking $\binom{n}{r}$ and $\binom{n}{n-r}$.

10. For what values, if any, of n and r is $\binom{n+1}{r} = \binom{n}{r} + \binom{n}{r-1}$?

11. If $\binom{n}{r} = \binom{n}{s}$, what can be said about r and s?

12. If $\binom{n}{r} = \binom{m}{s}$, what can be said about n, r, m and s?

The quantity $\binom{n}{r}$ comes up all over Pascal's Triangle and there is a very good reason for this.

But let me take one step backwards. Expand $(x+1)^2$ and $(x+1)^3$.

Now $(x+1)^2 = (x+1)(x+1) = x^2 + 2x + 1$

$$(x+1)^3 = (x+1)^2(x+1) = \left(x^2 + 2x + 1\right)(x+1) = x^3 + 3x^2 + 3x + 1.$$

There's some sort of familiarity in all this. I've seen these numbers, the coefficients, somewhere before. Where else than in good old Pascal's Triangle?

With a bit of work it's clear (not that word again!) that

$$(x+1)^4 = \left(x^3 + 3x^2 + 3x + 1\right)(x+1) = x^4 + 4x^3 + 6x^2 + 4x + 1$$
$$(x+1)^5 = x^5 + 5x^4 + 10x^3 + 10x^2 + 5x + 1,$$

and so on.

Exercises

13. Check that $(x+1)^6$ and $(x+1)^7$ get their coefficients from Pascal's Triangle.

14. Prove that $(x+1)^n$ can be written in terms with $\binom{n}{r}$-type coefficients.

15. The terms in Pascal's Triangle always seem to be symmetric. It doesn't seem to matter whether you start at the left end or the right end, you meet the same terms in order. Can you prove that? Have you already proved that?

16. What value do you get when you add together all the numbers in a fixed row of Pascal's Triangle?

In view of Exercise 14 we have proved the following theorem which is known as the **Binomial Theorem**. The word "binomial" comes from the fact that it's a two (bi) numbers (nom) thing (ial). The two numbers are the x and the y.

Binomial Theorem

$$(x+y)^n = \sum_{r=0}^{n}\binom{n}{r}x^{n-r}y^r$$

Here the Σ is the summation sign that we found in Chapter 3. Just to check it out let's try expanding $(x+y)^4$. Now we know from Pascal's Triangle that

$$(x+y)^4 = x^4 + 4x^3y + 6x^2y^2 + 4xy^3 + y^4.$$

From the Binomial Theorem we have

$$(x+y)^4 = \sum_{r=0}^{4}\binom{4}{r}x^{4-r}y^r$$

$$= \binom{4}{0}x^{4-0}y^0 + \binom{4}{1}x^{4-1}y^1 + \binom{4}{2}x^{4-2}y^2 + \binom{4}{3}x^{4-3}y^3 + \binom{4}{4}x^{4-4}y^4$$

$$= 1.x^4.1 + 4x^3y + 6x^2y^2 + 4xy^3 + 1.1.y^4.$$

This is what we got from Pascal's Triangle.

Now about a proof. You might have already managed it in Exercise 15 but let's have another look.

Suppose we want to find the coefficient of $x^{n-r}y^r$ in the expansion of $(x+y)^n$. Now

$$(x+y)^n = \underbrace{(x+y)(x+y)\ldots(x+y)}_{n\text{ brackets}}.$$

How do we get $x^{n-r}y^r$? Well, we simply take a y from r of the n brackets. The x^{n-r} automatically comes from the remaining $n-r$ brackets. How many ways are there of getting y^r? As many ways as choosing r brackets from n brackets. That is $\binom{n}{r}$, or n choose r. So there are $\binom{n}{r}$ ways of getting $x^{n-r}y^r$. That many ways is just the coefficient of $x^{n-r}y^r$ and we're done. We now get the entire expansion by letting $r = 0, 1, 2, ..., n$ successively.

Incidentally, the terms $\binom{n}{r}$ are also known as Binomial Coefficients, for obvious reason.

Exercises

17. Check the Binomial Theorem by determining the expansion of $(x+y)^6$.

18. What is the expansion of $(x-y)^6$?

19. Expand $(x+2y)^5$.

20. Find $\displaystyle\sum_{r=0}^{n}\binom{n}{r}$.

8.2 *Words and Alphabets*

When we were looking at the Binomial Coefficients $\binom{n}{r}$, we were looking at n different objects. Let's think about objects where we have repetition or where we can't distinguish between some objects. The simplest example of this is to take an alphabet which just consists of A's and B's. Then we can ask how many "words" using three letters from our alphabet can we make.

Again, we can start out thinking about this by writing down a systematic list. This might look a bit like

				Total
(three A's)	AAA			1
(two A's)	AAB	ABA	BAA	3
(one A)	ABB	BAB	BBA	3
(no A's)	BBB			$\dfrac{1}{8}$

So we probably have 8 "words" using the two letters A and B. Actually the interesting thing about the list is that it goes 1, 3, 3, 1. Doesn't that seem very binomial to you?

Exercises

21. (a)   How many words with four letters can be made from our alphabet?
    (b)   Suppose the alphabet has three letters A, B, C. How many words can we make
           with five letters?
    (c)   Generalise.

One way to look at the expansion of $(x+y)^3$ gives us the wordcount that we were looking for.

$$(x+y)^3 = x^3 + 3x^2y + 3xy^2 + y^3.$$

Well, maybe it's clearer if we use the letters of our two letter alphabet.

$$(A+B) = A^3 + 3A^2B + 3AB^2 + B^3.$$

It's no accident that the coefficient of A^3 is 1 which is the number of three letter words made up just from A. On the other hand, there are 3 words which have two A's (the coefficient of A^2B and so on. But what is the correspondence here? Why, in general, is $\binom{n}{r}$ the number of n letter words from a two-letter alphabet where one letter is used r times?

However, that's not really the interesting thing here. The fact is that $\sum_{r=0}^{n}\binom{n}{r} = 2^n$, so there are 2^n words of length n that you can make from a two-letter alphabet.

Of course you knew that already. It's quite simple, really. There are two choices for the first letter of the word, two choices for the second letter, and so on up to the nth and last letter. So the number of words is

$$\underbrace{2 \times 2 \times ... \times 2}_{n \text{ times}} = 2^n.$$

Generalising this is a breeze. If there are m letters in the alphabet, the number of n-letter words is $\underbrace{m \times m \times ... \times m}_{n \text{ times}} = m^n$ by the same sort of argument we've just used. (There are m choices for the first letter, m choices for the second letter, ...). But it's interesting to look at the case for $m = 3$. Is there an expansion like $(A+B)^3$ which will give us all the n-letter words we want?

Exercises

22.   Why does the expansion of $(A+B)^3$ have anything to do with the words of length 3 on an
       alphabet of size 2?

23.   How many words of length 4 are there on an alphabet of size 2, where no two A's are
       next to each other?

Suppose we had an alphabet of 3 letters, A, B, C. What does $(A+B+C)^2$ look like? We've talked about binomials, so what about a **tri**nomial?

$$(A+B+C)^2 = (A+B+C)(A+B+C)$$
$$= (A+B)^2 + 2(A+B)C + C^2, \text{ keeping } (A+B) \text{ together}$$
$$= A^2 + 2AB + B^2 + 2AC + 2BC + C^2$$
$$= A^2 + B^2 + C^2 + 2(AB + BC + CA).$$

Why do we know those coefficients in advance? What are the terms we get when we expand $(A+B+C)^4$. Is there a Trinomial Theorem?

Exercises
24. Expand $(A+B+C)^4$.

    What can you say in advance about the coefficient of AB^2C?
25. Can you find, state, and prove the Trinomial Theorem?
    Is there a Multinomial Theorem?

Now a useful variation on two-letter alphabets is 0-1 sequences. These are things like 010011101011. If you want to know how many 0-1 sequences you can make of length 5, that's equivalent to the number of 5-letter words on a 2 letter alphabet. And the answer is 2^5. But 0-1 sequences are often a nice way to count things. Here are a few examples.

Example 1
How many solutions are there of the equation $x + y + z = 15$, where x, y, z are all non-negative integers?

You might like to have a think about that before reading how 0-1 sequences come to the rescue. In fact, to help you keep our eyes off of the solution, I'll give you another example first.

Example 2
How many 15-letter words can be produced from an alphabet which has three letters?

That's another one to try. And at this stage you might like to see if you can outsmart me. There really is a great similarity between those last two examples. They've both got 15; they've both got 3. What does your intuition tell you? Did I choose them because they are the same or is it a trick?

Let's get down to Example 1. The neat way to get this that I hope you've discovered is to use 15 ones and 2 zeros. The point of using the zeros is to hold the 15 ones apart. Look at this sequence.

　　　111101111110111111

We can use that to represent the solution $x = 4$, $y = 6$ and $z = 5$ of the equation $x + y + z = 15$. Every sequence of 15 ones and 2 zeros gives a solution of $x + y + z = 15$ and can be written as a 0-1 sequence. For instance, $x = 9$, $y = 6$, $z = 0$ becomes

　　　111111111011111110.

So there's an equivalence between the 0-1 sequences and the solutions. Counting 0-1 sequences ought to be easy, shouldn't it?

Exercises
26. Finish solving Example 1.
27. Did you get the same answer for Example 2? Why?
28. Find how many non-negative integer solutions there are of $x + y + z + w = 22$.
29. How many positive integer solutions there are of $x + y + z = 15$?
30. Suppose x, y, z are integers with $x \geq 3$, $y \geq 4$ and $z \geq 5$. How many solutions are there of $x + y + z = 15$?

Which gets us round to Example 2. If we try 0-1 sequences we would be sure to use 111110110111111111 to represent AAAAABBCCCCCCCC. Which is fine, but it doesn't tell us how many 15-letter words there are because we don't have a way of expressing AAAABBCCCCCCCCA as a 0-1 sequence. Well we might, but it wouldn't be a sequence of 2 zeros and 15 ones! Sorry, it was a trick. But nothing is ever done without reason. And you ought to have known what was going on anyway, if you had done Exercise 25.

8.3   *Essential Skills*

This is the section in which we review the new mathematical skills that you might need in the problems that are coming up. As always, don't abandon any skills you've had before. You never know when they will come in handy.

Counting with repetition
The number of ways of choosing n objects from m objects where each object may be used as often as needed is m^n.

Binomial Coefficients
The number of ways of choosing r objects from a set of n objects is $\dbinom{n}{r} = \dfrac{n!}{r!(n-r)!}$.

It is worth knowing that $\binom{n}{0} = 1 = \binom{n}{n}$ and $\binom{n}{r} = \binom{n}{n-r}$.

Binomial Theorem: $(x+y)^n = \sum_{r=0}^{n} \binom{n}{r} x^{n-r} y^r$.

Multinomial Coefficients

The number of ways of ordering n objects where r_1 of them are of one type, r_2 of them are of another type, ..., r_s of them are of another type, and $\sum_{i=1}^{s} r_i = n$ is $\dfrac{n!}{r_1! r_2! \ldots r_3!}$.

Multinomial Theorem

$(x_1 + x_2 + \cdots + x_5)^n = \sum \dfrac{n!}{r_1! r_2! \cdots r_3!} x_1^{r_1} x_2^{r_3} \cdots x_x^{r_s}$. Here the summation is taken over all sums

$\sum_{i=1}^{s} r_i$ so that $\sum_{i=1}^{s} r_i = n$.

8.4   Problem Solving Skills

Apart from the obvious strategy of reading the question carefully, there are a couple of techniques that might come in especially useful when you are stuck.

Making a **systematic list** has already been useful in the first two sections of this chapter. Why would you want to do that? Well, it's a good strategy for getting the answer. So that's a pretty good reason not to knock it. On the other hand, you might not be sufficiently enthusiastic to write down all non-negative solutions of $x + y + z = 15$, even if it can be done by 0-1 sequences. Having said that, I've been involved with competitions where young students, who perhaps didn't know any better, wrote down all 189 solutions of the following problem.

Example 3

How many of the numbers between 100 and 1997, have the same hundreds digit as their ones digit?

You might like to think how to find the solution more quickly using a slightly more sophisticated method.

But the other reason for writing a systematic list is to get an idea of how you might tackle the problem in a better way. Computers are good at making systematic lists but even they run out of room if the problem gets too big. However, there are big problems that can fall to simple techniques - once you've found them. And making systematic lists sometimes helps.

There is another strategy that often goes with systematic lists, and that is, use a **simpler problem**. You may not want to write down all the solutions to $x+y+z=15$, but you could probably be tempted to try $x+y+z=5$. There shouldn't be too many solutions there. On the other hand, if you can solve the $x+y+z=5$ problem, it's probably not too difficult to hop up to $x+y+z=15$. So the systematic list on the simpler $x+y+z=5$ may give you inspiration to find a straightforward technique that can be extended up to $x+y+z=15$ or even $x+y+z=155555555$!

8.5   *Uncountable Problems*

Way back in Chapter 5, we introduced graphs. Now let's try to count them. I've listed two sorts below. One of these is called graphs and the other unlabelled graphs. Two labelled graphs are considered the same if you can match them up so that corresponding labelled vertices are in the same position. The same sort of thing holds for unlabelled graphs.

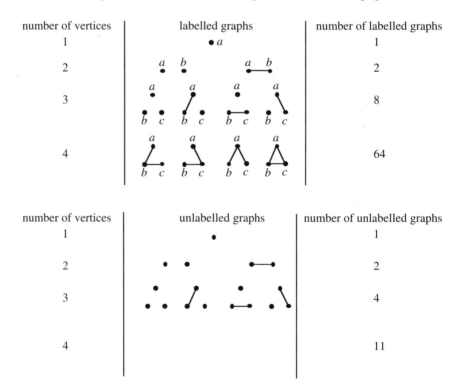

number of vertices	labelled graphs	number of labelled graphs
1		1
2		2
3		8
4		64

number of vertices	unlabelled graphs	number of unlabelled graphs
1		1
2		2
3		4
4		11

We leave you to convince yourself that we've got the right number of graphs in each case.

Now the interesting thing here is that labelled graphs are a cinch to count. The number of labelled graphs on n vertices is 2^p where $p = \dfrac{n(n-1)}{2}$ or $\dbinom{n}{2}$. I'll let you work that out for yourselves. So that's nice, and fairly straightforward.

Unlabelled graphs on the other hand are a real pain. There is no simple way known to count all the unlabelled graphs on n vertices. There is no simple formula involving n which will sort this one out for you. That's not to say there is no formula. Pólya gave an enumeration technique which will tell you the number of unlabelled graphs with n vertices. However, it's so complicated and difficult to use that you might as well produce a systematic list.

There are other counting problems to do with graphs that are as yet uncountable, in the sense that we can't count them. One of these is related to Ramsey's Theorem. The counts we would like are called **Ramsey numbers**.

In order to think about these we need to define the graph K_n. This is the complete graph on n vertices. All $\dfrac{n(n-1)}{2}$ edges are present. I've shown K_n for $n \leq 5$ in Figure 2.

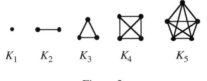

$$K_1 \qquad K_2 \qquad K_3 \qquad K_4 \qquad K_5$$

Figure 2

Now for reasons I don't have time to go into, Ramsey wanted to know how big n would have to be, so that if edges of K_n were coloured randomly either red or blue, there would have to be either a red K_3 or a blue K_3.

You can see from Figure 3, that n has to be bigger than 5. In the figure we show one way of colouring the edges so that there is no monochromatic K_3.

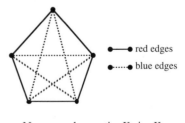

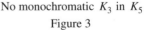
red edges
blue edges

No monochromatic K_3 in K_5

Figure 3

It turns out that $n = 6$ and there's a relatively nice argument to prove it.

Suppose you want to colour each of the edges of K_6 either red or blue. Look at one of the vertices. It has five edges coming out of it. So no matter how you colour these edges you must have either at least three red edges or at least three blue edges. Without loss of generality, assume they are red edges. (If not, we go back over the argument replacing red by blue and blue by red.) We show this in Figure 4.

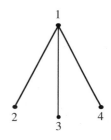

three red edges

Figure 4

Now think about the edge 23. If this is red, then we have our monochromatic K_3. To ward off the evil triangle assume 23 is blue. But for the same reason, 24 is blue. For the same reason 34 is blue. Hang on there! Now we've got a blue K_3 joining 2, 3, and 4. So K_6 must have a monochromatic K_3.

You might like to go back through this argument to check it out. It's a fairly subtle argument that may worry you at first sight. One thing that might upset you is the fact that we haven't used vertices 5 and 6 in Figure 4. Well actually we have. In order to know that there are three red or blue edges coming out of vertex 1, we needed to know that there were six vertices to start with. The argument fails in K_5 because we can have two red edges and two blue edges coming out of each vertex. That's what enabled us to draw Figure 3 and know that we needed $n > 5$.

So the Ramsey number for two monochromatic K_3's is 6 and we've been able to count that fairly easily. What is the Ramsey number for two monochromatic K_4's? Or what is the Ramsey number for monochromatic K_3's when the edges are coloured in red, white and blue? What if we use seven colours and insist on a monochromatic K_{10}?

The point I'm trying to make is that there are currently notoriously difficult things to count. Armies of computers are probably trying to find the next smallest Ramsey number as we speak! If you like counting and fancy making a name for yourself, then try counting Ramsey numbers.

Problems

If you get stuck on a problem, there are some hints beginning on page 117.

1.   The coefficients of x^5 and x^{15} in the expansion of $(1+x)^n$ are equal, where n is a positive integer. Find the value of n.

2.   Let $f(x) = (1+x) + (1+x)^2 + (1+x)^3 + \ldots + (1+x)^{100}$. What is the coefficient of x^{98} in $f(x)$?

3.   When the integers from 1 to n are written in order the total number of digits used is 2400. What is n?

4.   (a)   When a two-digit number and a three-digit number are multiplied, the result is 7777. Find the largest such three-digit number possible.

      (b)   Find the smallest multiple of 49 which has all of its digits the same.

5.   A sequence t_1, t_2, t_3 is formed by choosing t_1 at random from the set $\{1, 2, 3\}$, t_2 at random from the set $\{4, 5, 6\}$, and t_3 at random from the set $\{7, 8, 9\}$. What is the probability that t_1, t_2, t_3 is an arithmetic sequence?

6.   How many numbers in the set $\{10, 11, 12, \ldots, 99\}$ increase in value when the order of their digits is reversed?

7.   How many permutations are there of all the digits $1, 2, 3, \cdots, 9$ in which the first is an odd digit and the last is one of 1, 2, 3, 4?

8.   If 332, 520, and 755 are each divided by d (an integer greater than one), the remainder r is the same. Determine the value of $d + r$.

9.   There are four different French books, six different Spanish books, and seven different German books. How many ways are there of arranging the books on a shelf if all books of the same language are grouped together?

10.   What is the probability that an arrangement of the letters a, b, c, d, e, f has
      (a) a and b side by side?
      (b) a ahead of b in the arrangement?

11.   Show that any odd perfect square can be written in the form $8k + 1$, for some integer k.

12.   The integers 1, 2, 3, 4, 5, 6, 7 are arranged at random to form a seven-digit number.
      (a)   Determine the probability that the number formed is odd.
      (b)   Determine the probability that the number formed is less than 3 200 000.
      (c)   Determine the probability that the number formed is divisible by 4.

      Explain your answers.

13.   How many ways are there to distribute nine different books among six students such that every student gets at least one book and no student gets more than two books?

14. If 5 fair coins are tossed, what is the probability that at least two heads occur?

15. There are 20 volumes of an encyclopedia on a shelf. In how many ways can 5 of these volumes be selected if no two consecutive volumes are chosen?

16. A right-angled triangle has sides whose lengths are two-digit integers. The digits of the length of the hypotenuse are the reverse of the digits of the length of one of the other sides. Determine the smallest possible length of the hypotenuse.

17. Find the number of ways of arranging all the letters $AAABBBCCDD$ in a row so that no two B's are side-by-side.

18. All of the digits 1, 2, 3, ..., 8 are permuted. For any permutation, the eight digits now occupy positions 1 to 8 in some order.
    (a) In how many of these permutations is the product of the digits in all sets of five consecutive positions divisible by 5?
    (b) In how many of these permutations is the product of the digits in all pairs of adjacent positions divisible by 2?

19. Consider sequences of length n, $n \geq 1$, formed using two letters H and T, given an unlimited supply of each.
    (a) How many such sequences are possible?
    (b) How many such sequences are possible in which there is no occurrence of "HT"?
    (c) How many such sequences are possible in which there is exactly one occurrence of "HT"?

20. Find the number of terms in the expansion of $(a+b+c+d)^{10}$.

Chapter 9   Challenge Problems

9.1   Where to Now?

At the end of Chapter 1, I talked about extensions and generalisations and said that these were the lifeblood of mathematics. It probably needs to be said that mathematics started off with the aim of solving problems that existed in the "real" world. In a sense that has been the case and always will be the case.

But mathematics also generates mathematics. Having solved a problem, a mathematician will generalise and extend and very often soon be a long way from the original problem. In the process, she or he will have developed a lot of new, sometimes interesting, sometimes valuable results. Surprisingly, these results which may often have become quite abstract and no longer connected to anything in the "real" world, will be found to have important applications. For instance, Euclid developed an algorithm that had to do with finding the highest common factor (or greatest common divisor) of two numbers. His Euclidean Algorithm appeared in his **Elements** getting on to 2000 years ago. Then 200 years or so ago, Euler found another result to do with certain remainders of powers of a number. Both of these results were useful in mathematics. However, it wasn't until the 1970s that Rivest, Shamir, and Adleman put the two things together to produce a **public key** cryptography system. This is a coding system where you can tell anyone how to **encode** a message to you but that it is almost impossible for anyone else to **decode**!

So, many abstractions by mathematicians do eventually lead back to useful applications. Having justified the point of mathematics (although some people are happy with the idea that the only point of mathematics is to produce more mathematics), let's see how mathematics reproduces itself.

In Chapter 1, I spent some time finding mathmarks. These are ways of filling in circles with numbers from 1 to 6, so that the sums of the numbers on each side of the equilateral triangle were the same.

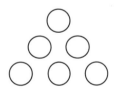

Figure 1

Recall from Chapter 1 that if I ignore rotations there are precisely four mathmarks, which I'll call Mathmarks with a capital M. I've shown these in Figure 2.

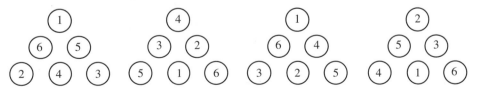

Figure 2

The first big generalisation of Mathmarks is to find all sets of six numbers which could be put, one per circle, and still have the sums on each side the same. I'll call such a set of numbers **nice** and the Mathmarks they produce, **Mathmarks$^+$**. I already know that $\{1, 2, 3, 4, 5, 6\}$ is nice. And we can show that **any** set of six consecutive numbers is nice. For instance $\{54, 55, 56, 57, 58, 59\}$ is nice because I can take any Mathmark and add 53 to each of the numbers 1 through 6.

What sets of numbers are nice? Before we really get going on this I should point out that this is only a mildly interesting problem. Once I've solved it, if I can, it's not going to set the world on fire. It's got absolutely no applications whatsoever, as far as I know. However, it might give you some idea of what a generalisation is and how such a problem is solved.

Exercises
1.   What sets of numbers are nice?
2.   If Exercise 1 is too hard, find as many sets of nice numbers as you can.

If you play around for a while you'll first see that not only is the set of any six consecutive numbers nice but so too is the set of any six numbers in arithmetic progression. Think about $A = \{a, a + d, a + 2d, a + 3d, a + 4d, a + 5d\}$. You could start off with a Mathmark and subtract one from each number. This gives $\{0, 1, 2, 3, 4, 5\}$ as nice. I think it is then clear that $\{0, d, 2d, 3d, 4d, 5d\}$ is nice.

Exercises
3.   Show that $\{3, 7, 11, 15, 19, 23\}$ is nice by exhibiting four different Mathmarks$^+$.
4.   What possible side sums can $A = \{a, a + d, a + 2d, a + 3d, a + 4d, a + 5d\}$ produce?
5.   Are there sum numbers which can't be a side sum for A?

I don't know if you can see where I'm going but I'm actually casting around for ideas. This is a sort of **exploratory** stage where I'm trying to get a feel for the problem. By playing around with a lot of examples, I'll be able to make an intelligent guess as to what the answer might be. As I am actually far too sophisticated and important a person to make guesses, I'll call them **conjectures** instead. From what I've done so far, it looks to me as if I might have a good conjecture already.

Conjecture
If N is a nice set, then $N = A$.

Exercises
6.   What do you think of this conjecture? Is it true or is it false?
7.   If this conjecture is true, then prove it. If this conjecture is false, then what do you do next?

If this conjecture is true, then I can say that N is a nice set if and only if $N = A$. In other words if N is nice then $N = A$ and if $N = A$ is N is nice. The last implication "if $N = A$, then N is nice" I have already proved. So I only have to prove the implication of the conjecture.

One small point here; this "if and only if" business, that you sometimes see written "iff", is an equivalence. It tells you that the statement "N is a nice set" is equivalent to "$N = A$".

Pythagoras' Theorem is like this. It says that a, b, c form the three sides of a right-angled triangle if and only if $a^2 + b^2 = c^2$. Some people put it in terms of necessary and sufficient conditions. They say that a necessary and sufficient condition for a, b, c to be three sides of a right-angled triangle, is that $a^2 + b^2 = c^2$.

Well, if you remember, I have this conjecture. What do I do with it now? If it's true, of course, then I know all about nice sets. If it's false, though, what do I do?

Now, how do I know if the conjecture is true? Well, I just have to prove it. That actually may be harder than you think.

On the other hand, if the conjecture is false, I may be able to find a **counterexample**. A counterexample is a set which is nice and whose elements are **not** in arithmetic progression. Counterexamples can be as difficult to find as proofs. So it's never clear whether it's easier to find a proof or a counterexample. Of course, if the conjecture's true, there won't be a counterexample to find. However, if it's false, there won't be a proof. So which direction should I go?

In practice it may not matter too much. Sometimes trying to find a proof leads to a counterexample. Sometimes trying to find a counterexample leads to a proof. (Sorry to be so helpful.)

I've decided to go down the counterexample road. And in doing this, I'll try an extreme example first. Let $M = \{1, 2, 3, 4, 5, 100\}$. That isn't an A set. But it's probably not nice either. Surely that 100 is too large for side sums to be the same.

So can we be less extreme? What is the smallest non-arithmetic progression set of six numbers.

Exercises

8.   Is $M = \{1, 2, 3, 4, 5, 7\}$ nice?
9.   What about $M = \{1, 2, 3, 4, 5, 8\}$?
10. If the M's of the last two Exercises are not nice, then the conjecture still holds. Prove it. If either M is nice, try to find another conjecture.

The last Exercise tells you how I have to proceed. Did you manage to settle Exercise 8? Is it proof or new conjecture time?

Of course, there is another way to look at this. We could try assuming that some abstract set $M = \{a, b, c, d, e, f\}$ is nice and see what that tells us about the relative values of a, b, c, d, e, f. We then might produce some conditions that could turn out to be necessary and sufficient.

In Figure 3, I've assumed that $M = \{a, b, c, d, e, f\}$ is nice. What conclusions can I reach? I think I know the following things.

$$a+b+c = c+d+e = e+f+a.$$

If you prefer that as three equations, see below where s is the side sum.

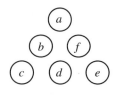

Figure 3

$$\left. \begin{array}{l} a+b+c = s \\ c+d+e = s \\ e+f+a = s \end{array} \right\} \quad (1)$$

But that's three equations in seven unknowns. Am I likely to get very far solving those?

Well I suppose we're hardly likely to be able to find specific values for a, b, c, d, e, f. After all, we know that there are infinitely many possible sets. (Take any arithmetic progression.) So the best we can hope for is some relation between the six variables.

Exercises
11.   What relations can we find between the six unknowns? What help is this?
12.   Does the last Exercise help us to find a new conjecture?

Having thought about the problem a bit more, it seems to me that in the original nice sets I had six different numbers. So perhaps I should agree that a, b, c, d, e, f are different too, I don't think this is going to be much of a restriction.

Ah! And earlier on I had $(a+b+c)+(c+d+e)+(e+f+a) = 3s$, so $(a+b+c+d+e+f)+(a+c+f) = 3s$.

Is that really any help? It's only a restatement of equations (1). If I subtract pairs of equations (1) from each other, I get

$$a+b-(d+e) = 0$$
$$c+d-(f+a) = 0$$
$$e+f-(b+c) = 0$$

$$\text{or} \quad \left.\begin{array}{l} a+b=d+e \\ c+d=f+a \\ e+f=b+c \end{array}\right\} \quad (2)$$

Let me see. Does knowing a, b, c, d, e give me f?

Exercises
13.   Show that if I know a, b, c, d, e, then I know f.
14.   Is it true that if I know a, b, c, d, then I know e and f?
15.   If I know three of M, will that give me the other three?
16.   If I know two of M, will that give me the other four?

It's just come to me. You may have realised it already back in Chapter 1. Figure 3 gives me another Mathmark$^+$. I've put them together in Figure 4.

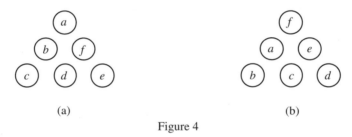

(a)   (b)

Figure 4

From the set of equations (2) on the previous page, it is easy to see that if $a+b=d+c$ then $a+b+f=d+e+f$, and so $a+b+f=d+e+f=b+c+d$.

That means the Mathmark$^+$ in Figure 4(a) implies the Mathmark$^+$ in Figure 4(b), and vice-versa.

Exercises
17.   Show that the Mathmark$^+$ of Figure 4(b) implies the Mathmark$^+$ of Figure 4(a).
18.   What is the significance of Figure 4?

What I've been looking for is some simplification. I needed a handle on this problem and it wasn't coming. One way of using Figure 4 is to find the smallest number. Suppose $a<c$ and $a<e$. It may still be the case that b, d or f is smaller than a. However, if this is the case, I just move all the numbers around, as in Figure 4(b). This way the smallest number must be in a corner. Without loss of generality then, I can assume that a is the smallest number.

From equation (2): $a + b = d + e$,

so $d = a + (b - e)$.

Let me assume that $b - e = \beta$. I'm not sure what β is. It may be positive or negative (but it can't be zero).

Again from equation (2): $c + d = f + a$.

Hence $c + a + \beta = f + a$.

This means that $f = c + \beta$.

And again from equation (2): $e + f = b + c$.

Hence $e + c + \beta = b + c$.

So we have $b = e + \beta$.

I can now rewrite Figure 4(a) (see Figure 5).

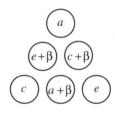

Figure 5

I think what this tells me is that if a is the smallest member of a nice set, and c, e are two other members, then the other members of the set are $a + \beta$, $c + \beta$, $e + \beta$ for some number $\beta \neq 0$. Then how's this for a new conjecture?

New Conjecture

Let a be the smallest member of M. M is a nice set if and only if
$M = \{a, c, e, a + \beta, c + \beta, e + \beta\}$.

Now I haven't put $\beta = 0$ because I've just remembered that for these sets, every element is distinct. So $a, c, e, a + \beta, c + \beta, e + \beta$ have to be all different.

Exercises

19.   What do you think of this new Conjecture? Prove the new Conjecture or find a counterexample.

20.   In the new conjecture, is c the second smallest element and e the third smallest? (Try to make Mathmarks[+] where neither c nor e is the second smallest element of M.)

I must have proved part of the new conjecture in the lead up to the last set of Exercises. Which part did I prove? What did I assume? I guess I assumed that M was nice because I assumed a Mathmark$^+$ existed. So I have already proved that if M is nice, then $M = \{a, c, e, a+\beta, c+\beta, e+\beta\}$. Does the implication in the other direction hold? Suppose $M = \{a, c, e, a+\beta, c+\beta, e+\beta\}$. Then is M nice? Surely it must be. I have Figure 5 to prove it. So the new conjecture is true. I must therefore have a Theorem.

Exercises

21.   Write out the proof of the new conjecture in full.
      Does the proof require a to be the **smallest** element of M?

22.   Let $M = \{a, c, e, a+\beta, c+\beta, e+\beta\}$. Does M only give **two** Mathmarks$^+$? (See Figure 4.) Why is it that $\{1, 2, 3, 4, 5, 6\}$ gives **four** Mathmarks$^+$? What extra relationships have to hold for M to give **four** Mathmarks$^+$?

23.   Use the Theorem to test whether $\{1, 2, 3, 4, 5, 7\}$ and $\{1, 2, 3, 4, 5, 8\}$ are nice.

24.   Can you generalise this problem further?

Now you might see how mathematics develops. A common progression is shown in Figure 6. First we have a problem. We play around (explore) to get a guess (conjecture). We then prove the conjecture or find a counterexample. (If the problem is too hard we may have to give up.) A proof leads to a theorem and then we try to generalise or extend again. (Or go on to a new problem.) A counterexample leads back to more explorations and around we go again.

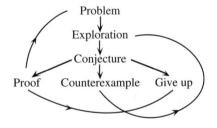

Figure 6

And so it goes on.

Exercise

25.   Take the 13-puzzle and generalise.
      The 13-puzzle says put the number 1 to 9 in the squares so that the rows and columns add to 13.

      (a)   Using the numbers 1 to 9, what other totals (besides 13) are possible?

      (b)   Let M be any set of nine numbers. Let a set be **fine** if the numbers can be put into the squares so that the row and column sums are always the same. Find necessary and sufficient conditions for M to be fine.

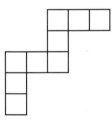

9.2   *Difficult Problems*

When is a problem difficult? Well, it's difficult if you can't do it. But I guess that only means that it is difficult for *you*! So, for a problem to be difficult, it has to be difficult for your friends as well and for a lot of other people too. Of course you may not realise that at the time, so I'll concentrate on what *you* may find difficult.

So what might make a problem difficult? There are probably at least three answers to that question. The first thing that may cause difficulties is that you can't see how to go from the words of the problem to some mathematical method. In a case like this it may not be clear whether to use algebra or counting techniques or whatever. You may have overlooked some important piece of information.

The next thing that might make a problem hard is that it may require some technically difficult mathematics. For instance, it may require some derivative that you haven't seen before.

And the third thing may be that, even if you can set things up and do the appropriate mathematical algorithm, you may still not be able to see how to put the pieces together. There may be a number of steps involved in getting a complete solution and the steps may be quite intricate. You may not be able to see how to assemble all the bits together.

The important thing to remember is that, even with difficult problems, the same general problem solving strategies come into play. So, if you have banged your head against a mathematical brick wall for a while, you should stop and consider what to do and where to go next. Here is a checklist that might be helpful.

1.   Read the question
I don't mean just read the question, I mean *read the question*. It's sometimes a good idea to highlight what seem to be the key factors in the problem. Check to see if there are any hidden assumptions.

2.   Possible strategies
- Have you seen a problem like this somewhere else? Recalling that might help.
- Keep a mental list of the strategies discussed throughout this book.
- What type of mathematics might help? Is it algebra, trigonometry, geometry, counting, what?
- Look for sub-problems; by breaking it down you can often crack the whole thing. For instance, a problem in calculus might involve first finding the equation of a line. That's simple enough.
- Experiment; play around with the problem; look for special cases
- Draw a diagram whenever possible.

3. Seek Help

Don't be shy about asking for help. Here are some suggestions.

- Talk to one of your friends who may know something about the problem. Actually one of the best ways to get on top of many things in life, is to talk about them with a group of friends. Mathematical problems are no different from other problems in this respect.
- Even if your mother or father or brother or sister know nothing about mathematics, tell them about your problem. It's amazing how often I have found that talking to my wife (a total non-mathematician) has helped me to understand a problem. The act of verbalising things really seems to help. So don't be afraid to do that as a first step. (If no one else is around, it's useful to talk to yourself. You'll be surprised how much you know that you didn't know).
- If that doesn't work, ask an expert. You could try one of your teachers. You might even write a letter to the math department at a local university.
- If you have still drawn a blank, then give up. One of the important tools in mathematics is to give up. When you are least expecting it, a key idea may jump into your head. A famous mathematician called Poincaré once had a brilliant idea when stepping on to a bus. So it does work, believe me.
- If all else fails, then look up the answer in the book. But don't do that until you have spent quite a bit of effort trying to get the problem yourself. And if you do have to look up the answer, do it intelligently. Cover all but the first few lines. That may be enough for you to see how to solve the rest of the problem. If it isn't, look at and try to understand the whole answer. Then come back in a few days to see if the idea has really sunk in. You never know, that solution idea may be useful in another problem sometime later.

Now the reason for talking about difficult problems is that this final set are supposed to be harder than the questions in the earlier chapters. I hope that you won't find them all that troublesome. If you do though, you might consider the words of widsom above. I hope they help. If not, you'd better write to me and let me know.

I hope you enjoyed doing the Exercises and the problems, and that you now know a bit more about mathematics than you did before you started. Good luck!

Problems

If you get stuck on a problem, there are some hints beginning on page 117.

1. Two points P and Q move along the circumference of a circle at constant rates. They start at the same point A, and at the same time. If they move in opposite directions, they meet every 6 seconds. If they move in the same direction, they meet every 24 seconds. If the circumference of the circle is 360 cm, find the rate at which each point moves.

2. In triangle ABC, given that $b \cos A = a \cos B$ prove that $a = b$.

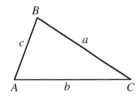

3. Consider the function $f(x) = \dfrac{(x+k)^2}{x^2+1}$, $-\infty < x < \infty$, where k is a constant and $k > 0$. Prove that $f(x) \le k^2 + 1$.

4. Suppose that point P lies inside triangle ABC, with PA of length 4, PB of length 2 and PC of length 1.
    (a) If $\angle APB = \angle BPC = \angle CPA$, prove that $\angle ACB = 90°$.
    (b) If $\angle ACB = 90°$ and $\angle APB = \angle BPC$, prove that $\angle CPA = 120°$.

5. (a) A sequence has nth term $a_n = 2^n k + 1$, where k is a fixed integer. Show that there is no prime, p, such that every term of the sequence is divisible by p.

    (b) For the sequence defined in part (a), show that there are no two primes, p and q, such that every term of the sequence is divisible by either p or q.

6. Determine all values of x which minimize $y = 6|x-3|^2 - 4|x-3| + 3$. What is this minimum?

7. In the given quadrilateral, the lengths of the sides are 34, 6, 33 and 47, respectively. Show that the diagonals are perpendicular.

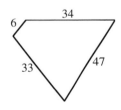

8. Ann and Bob play a game in which Ann starts by rolling a fair die and then Bob tosses a fair coin. They repeat this alternating pattern until one of them wins. Ann wins if a "six" occurs and Bob wins of a "head" occurs.
    (a) What is the probability that Ann wins the game?
    (b) The expected number of times that Ann rolls the die is given by

    $$E = \sum_{k=1}^{\infty} k[p(k) + q(k)], \text{ where } p(k) \text{ is the probability that Ann wins on her } k\text{th roll}$$

    and $q(k)$ is the probability that Bob wins on his kth toss. Evaluate E.

9.   Consider the concentric circles with equations
     $x^2 + y^2 = 4$ and $x^2 + y^2 = 9$. A radius from the
     centre O intersects the inner circle at P and the outer
     circle at Q. The line parallel to the x-axis through P
     meets the line parallel to the y-axis through Q at the
     point R. Prove that R lies on the

     ellipse $\dfrac{x^2}{9} + \dfrac{y^2}{4} = 1$.

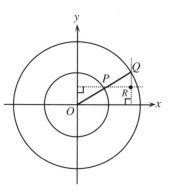

10. A *dominating permutation* of a collection of integers is a permutation of all these integers
     such that no integer has two immediate neighbours both of which are larger than it.

     (a) Prove that the number of dominating permutations of 1, 2, 3, 4, ..., n, where $n \ge 1$, is
          2^{n-1}. (Example: if $n = 4$, then 1432 is allowed, but 3214 is not).

     (b) How many dominating permutations are there of the $n+1$ integers 1, 1, 2, 3, 4, ..., n,
          where $n > 1$? Justify your answer.

11. Show that there are exactly four triples of real numbers (a, b, c) such that a, b and c are the
     roots of the equation $x^3 + ax^2 + bx + c = 0$?

12. In the diagram given, suppose that $\angle ACD = \alpha$,
     $\angle BDA = 2\theta$, and $\angle BDC = \angle ADE$.   Prove that

     $AB = BC$ if and only if $\dfrac{\cos(\alpha - \theta)}{\cos(\alpha + \theta)} = 2$.

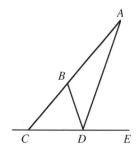

13. If k is a positive integer, determine the smallest positive value of k for which the equation
     $x^2 + kx = 4y^2 - 4y + 1$ has a solution (x, y), where both x and y are integers.

14. It is desired to create isosceles triangles having area A and perimeter P, where both A and P are **integers**.
    (a) If the equal sides have length x, determine the area function $A(x)$ in terms of P and x.
    (b) Determine the value of x for which $A(x)$ is a maximum and from this show that $P \geq 5$.
    (c) How many such triangles are there with integer area if $P = 20$?
    (d) How many such triangles are there in general?

15. A point P moves such that the sum of the distances from P to the coordinate axes is equal to the distance from P to the point $(1, 1)$.
    (a) Determine the equation of the locus of P.
    (b) Sketch the graph of the equation.

16. The sides of a triangle are 6, 8, and x. For what values of x is the triangle acute-angled?

17. Suppose p, q, r, s are fixed real numbers such that a quadrilateral can be formed with sides p, q, r, s in clockwise order. Prove that the vertices of the quadrilateral of maximum area lie on a circle.

18. Let $p = 2m - 1$, $q = 13m - 1$ and $r = 15m - 5$, where m is a positive integer. Note that if $m = 5$, p and q are perfect squares but r is not. If $m = 2$, q and r are perfect squares but p is not. Show that there is no value of m for which all of p, q and r are squares.

19. An arithmetic sequence S, has first term $t_1 = 4$ and the common difference $d = 3$.
    (a) Show that t_5, t_9 and t_{16} form a three-term geometric sequence.
    (b) Show that t_{21}, t_{37} and t_{65} also form a three-term geometric sequence with the same common ratio.
    (c) Prove that for all $k = 5 + 16p$, $p = 0, 1, 2, 3, ..., t_k$ is the first term in a three-term geometric sequence having the same common ratio as in parts (a) and (b) and each term is also a member of S.

20. Evaluate the sum of the logarithms (base 10) of all divisors of $1\,000\,000$.

Hints for Solving Selected Problems

Chapter 1

4. Draw the construction lines as illustrated. Then use Pythagoras to show that $(a+b)^2 = (a-b)^2 + (XY)^2$. Find similar expressions for $(a+c)^2$ and $(b+c)^2$.

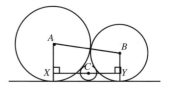

5. Try using four pieces each similar to the given shape.

6. Note that a pair of opposite corners of a chess board are the same colour.

Chapter 2

3. The line $y = mx + 4$ intersects the line $x = 3$ at the point $(3, 3m+4)$.

7. There are two solutions. Remember that two circles can touch either externally or internally.

11. The coordinates of B are of the form $(b, -2b)$. Why?

13. (b) The Cosine Law will be helpful.

15. Tangents drawn from an external point to a circle are equal in length. This will lead to one solution.

16. Adding the constant k to $f(x)$ has the effect of translating the graph of $f(x)$ vertically by k units.

17. Consider four cases. One case would be to impose the conditions that $y - x$ and x are both non-negative.

Chapter 3

5. Note that $f(n+1) - f(n) = \frac{1}{3}$, so $f(1), f(2), f(3), \dots$ forms an arithmetic sequence.

6. The exterior angles of the polygon form an arithmetic sequence whose sum is $360°$.

11. (b) For $n > 1$, $\dfrac{t_{n+1}}{t_n} = \dfrac{S_{n+1} - S_n}{S_n - S_{n-1}}$. Alternatively, begin by showing that $t_{n+1} = 2 \cdot 3^n$.

12. The sum of the first n odd integers is n^2.

15. The sum of the squares of the first n integers is $\dfrac{n(n+1)(2n+1)}{6}$. The inequality may also be proved directly using mathematical induction.

16. Let the nth terms of the two sequences be $t_n = a_1 + (n-1)d$ and $T_n = a_2 + (n-1)l$. Let their sums be S_n and R_n respectively. Then show that $\dfrac{t_{11}}{T_{11}} = \dfrac{S_{21}}{R_{21}}$.

17. Let the four parts be $a - 3d$, $a - d$, $a + d$, and $a + 3d$. (Why?)

Chapter 4

11. Remember that the start times are different. Consider each person's movement separately.

12. Factorise! It is often useful to know that $1 + x + x^2 + \cdots + x^k = \dfrac{1 - x^{k+1}}{1 - x}$.

13. Create a chart showing his movements.

14. Multiply it out. The resulting expression has factors.

16. A careful set-up for each train's time, distance, and speed is required.

17. What happens if the large hoses are used for one hour?

18. Start with the number of daily food allowances, and then consider how many are used on day 1, day 2, etc.

19. Be careful. The fence can be longer than the barn, but it also could be shorter than the barn; so think of two cases.

20. Use the fact that p is a root of the equation, then the fact that p is an integer. What does that tell you about the resulting expression? Now factor 630.

Chapter 5

2.   (c)   Multiply numerator and denominator of $\dfrac{1}{2^{1990}}$ by 2.

4.   Knowing the coordinates of one of the given points on the graph is sufficient to find a. For practice, show that you get the same result using the coordinates of all three points.

11.   Change to exponential form, then multiply both sides of the equation by 2^x.

12.   Multiply the numerator and denominator of the first fraction on the left side of the equation by e^x.

13.   Make a substitution; let $\dfrac{x}{n} = \dfrac{1}{m}$.

14.   Take logarithms, base 10, of both sides of the inequality.

15.   Since $\log_x a = m$, then $x^m = a$ and $x^{mn} = a^n$. Repeat with $\log_y a = n$ and then divide the results.

16.   Recall that $\log_e b = \ln b$. Use the "links between bases" that are given in the chapter discussion to change the form of $\dfrac{1}{\log_2 e}$, $\dfrac{1}{\log_3 e}$, and so on.

17.   To minimize the number of prizes we must have as many of the larger prizes as possible. You can do this just by using a calculator. Another approach that is pretty slick is to change 1 000 000 to base 11.

18.   The problem asks for a proof that there exists an integer satisfying the statement. It does **not** ask that a particular n be found, so the solution should focus on proving there is such an n.
Begin the proof by taking logarithms of the given double inequality.

19.   Assume that e is rational, that is, e can be written as a fraction in the form $\dfrac{a}{b}$. Then show that this leads to a contradiction. This contradiction arises from the fact that the difference between two integers cannot be a non-integer.
Start by writing $e = \dfrac{a}{b} = 1 + \dfrac{1}{1!} + \dfrac{1}{2!} + \cdots$, then multiply both sides by $b!$.

Chapter 6

8.   Remember the logarithm rules. The sum of the logs of two numbers is the log of their product.

10. A diagram is called for here.

12. While you can get fancy here, you require nothing more complex than the Theorem of Pythagoras.

13. Draw a diagram and get some trigonometric ratios.

14. Draw the graphs.

17. Simplify the equation and you'll get a quadratic equation. You will need to draw a triangle (right-angled, of course) to display the resulting values.

18. It's a quadratic equation, so use what you know about real roots.

20. Draw a diagram and on it show the basic facts of the rotation. You will see triangles that give you the result desired.

21. Find the mid-point of AB from the graphs. This allows you to get the coordinates of A and B and hence the rectangle's height.

Chapter 7

4.   Remember that $\dfrac{dy}{dx}$ represents the slope of the tangent and that this is itself a function, so it has a maximum.

6.   Draw a good diagram showing the lamp, the wall, and the person between them. You'll probably need to use implicit differentiation.

7.   Success here depends on assigning values for the coordinates of P in a smart way.

10. Find the equation of the tangent at P and see where it cuts the curve.

12. Find the circle areas and obtain $R(x)$. This is a function, which can be analyzed.

13. This is a little different from the usual type of problem. A diagram will help, and in part (b) try using the Law of Cosines.

15. A good diagram is a must. From it you can relate how long the shadow is to how far from the post the man is.

16. Draw a diagram. You'll see that you need the distances to be run and swum, and then the time required. Be careful in determining the distance CB. You may end up with an expression that is complicated. There is a fairly simple expression, though.

17. Again, a diagram gives you an idea of where to attack. You'll have to use $\tan(A+B)$ identity, so be careful.

Chapter 8

4. (b) Consider $N = k(1111\cdots)$, where N is divisible by 49.

11. An odd integer must be of the form $2n+1$. Why? Now square this and examine the result.

13. Consider first who gets two books.

14. How many outcomes are there? How many do not meet the condition?

15. Can you interpret this situation in terms of a's and b's? Let the a's represent the volumes selected in any ordering.

Chapter 9

3. You can frequently attack this type of inequality by considering the difference between the expressions; here, try $k^2 + 1 - f(x)$. Alternatively, look for a contradiction.

4. The Law of Cosines is a friend for many occasions. It will help you here in more than one way.

5. In part (a) look for a contradiction. In part (b) use what you get in part (a) and look for a second contradiction.

7. Try the Theorem of Pythagoras or some analytic geometry.

8. Do some experimentation. What is the probability that Ann wins on her first play? On her second play? You'll have to generalize, of course. In part (b), have courage. Just do what the definition tells you.

10. Part (a) should not cause you trouble. Simply consider where 1 can be, then 2, and so on. In part (b) consider cases by having the two 1's separated or together. Be careful with the second case because it depends on whether they are on the exterior or whether they are in the interior of the permutation.

11. The solution depends on the relations between the roots and the coefficients of the polynomial, then on examining cases for $c = 0$ and $c \neq 0$.

12. Use the Law of Sines, and don't be intimidated by awkward expressions for the angles.

13. There are at least two approaches. One uses properties of odd and even numbers (notice that the right side of the equation must be odd). The second, which you can start by completing the square on the left side, uses Pythagorean triples.

14. This looks like a geometry problem, but it is really about calculus and continuous functions.

15. You will have to consider cases. If you're careful, there are only two cases.

17. Draw in one diagonal and use the Cosine Law to relate the sides and the area of a triangle in terms of the sine of one angle, using opposite angles. This is a tough one.

18. Another contradiction example. Assume that there is a value for m and use the fact that p, q, r are all odd.

19. The first two parts are straightforward. In part (c) you must determine the terms and show that each belongs to S.

20. Remember that the sum of the logarithms is the logarithm of the product for a set of numbers. Now determine the divisors of the given number and proceed.

Answers for Exercises
Solutions to Problems

Chapter 1
Answers for Exercises

3. The side sums of the two mathmarks I've got so far are 9 and 12. How about trying side sums of 10 and 11? Can you do this systematically?

4. Well now there are a lot more possibilities. Doing this systematically you can put 1 anywhere you like. So there are six ways to do that. Then there are five circles left to put 2 in, four circles for 3, three circles for 4, two circles for 5, and one left over for the number 6. So altogether there are $6 \times 5 \times 4 \times 3 \times 2 \times 1 = 6! = 720$ unrestricted mathmarks.

   How does 720 compare with the answer you guessed to Exercise 1? So we now know that there must be less than 720 mathmarks. Or does every random placement of the numbers give us a mathmark? Surely not.

5. 6, 9, 12, 15

6. If the side sum is 10, the sum of the corners is $3 \times 10 - 21 = 9$.
   There are three ways for the corners to sum to 9. They are, working systematically
   $$1 + 2 + 6; \ 2 + 3 + 4; \ 1 + 3 + 5.$$
   There are no others because we can't repeat the same number.

   Try $1 + 2 + 6$
   For the left side to sum to 10 we would need a 7.
   Hence $1 + 2 + 6$ doesn't work.

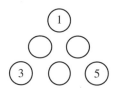

   Try $2 + 3 + 4$
   For the bottom side to sum to 10 we need another 3.
   There is no mathmark here.

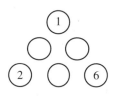

   Try $1 + 3 + 5$
   For the left side to sum to 10 we need to add a 6.
   For the right side we need a 4, and for the bottom a 2. This gives us a mathmark.

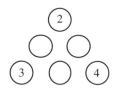

7. (i)   Since $\{a, b, c, d, e, f, g, h, i\} = \{1, 2, 3, 4, 5, 6, 7, 8, 9\}$,
          then $a + b + c + d + e + f + g + h + i = 45$.
          Now, let the sum of each vertical and horizontal
          row be Y.
          Then $(a + b + c) + (c + d + e) + (e + f + g) + (g + h + i) = 4Y$
          $$45 + 7 = 4Y$$
          $$13 = Y.$$

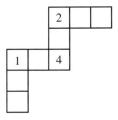

   (ii)   To find a particular Empmark we must find particular
          values of c, e, and g.
          First, note that $\{c, e, g\} = (1, 2, 4)$.
          But $\{c, e\} \neq \{1, 2\}$ because d would have to be 10.
          Similarly, $\{e, g\} = \{1, 2\}$.
          Hence $e = 4$.
          You should now be able to fill in the Empmark in
          several ways.

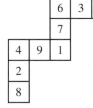

   (iii) From (a) we have $45 + (c + e + g) = 4Y$.
          The possible values of $c + e + g$ are 7, 11, 15, 19,
          and 23.

   (iv)

6	3	5	
	7		
4	9	1	
2			
8			

Solutions to Problems

1. Experiment. What conjecture do you have? How about 3¢, 5¢, 6¢ and everything else
    from 8¢ on? It's easy to show by trial and error that you can only get 3¢, 5¢ and 6¢
    below 8¢. How can you show that you can get everything from 8¢ onwards?
    Now $8 = 3 + 5$, $9 = 3 \times 3$ and $10 = 2 \times 5$. Since we can get three numbers in a row we can
    get any number of the form $8 + 3k$, $9 + 3k$ and $10 + 3k$. So we can get all numbers from
    8 onwards.

2. There are no one-digit reversibles ... except perhaps zero.
    Take the two-digit number $10a + b$. How can $9(10a + b) = 10b + a$. Note that $a < 2$
    since otherwise $9(10a + b)$ is a three-digit number. So $a = 1$ which forces b to be 9 (the
    only way to get a 1 on the end of a number when you multiply by 9). But $9 \times 19 \neq 91$!

    We could keep going on systematically doing three-digit, four-digit, ..., n-digit numbers.

But are you convinced that 1089 is the **only** reversible number? Hmmm!
1089 isn't the only one. We should have realised that 10891089, 10891, 0891089,
1089108910891089 are **all** reversible. But are **these** the only ones? Is it possible that
there is a five-digit reversible number?

3. $400 - ab4$ gives a 6 in the units column, so $b = 6$ (from the other subtraction).
      $400 - a64$ gives a 3 in the tens column, so $a = 3$ (from the other subtraction).
      Better just check that this is the right answer and nothing strange has happened.

4.   It's tempting to assume that $\triangle ABC$ is a right-
      angled triangle but it's not. But Pythagoras can
      run riot. You should be able to see that

      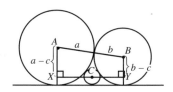

$$(a+b)^2 = (a-b)^2 + (XY)^2$$
$$(a+c)^2 = (a-c)^2 + (XC)^2$$
$$(b+c)^2 = (b-c)^2 + (CY)^2.$$

Then note that $XY = XC + CY$.

So $XY = \sqrt{(a+b)^2 - (a-b)^2} = 2\sqrt{ab}$

      $XC = 2\sqrt{ac}$ and $XY = 2\sqrt{bc}$.

Hence $2\sqrt{ab} = 2\sqrt{ac} + 2\sqrt{bc}$.

This leads to $\sqrt{c} = \dfrac{\sqrt{ab}}{\sqrt{a}+\sqrt{b}}$.

Finally $c = \dfrac{ab}{\left(\sqrt{a}+\sqrt{b}\right)^2}$.

5.   Is this the only solution though? By a shape I
      want one whole piece. No disconnected bits.
      Help, I can't answer this last question.

      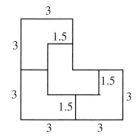

6.   Count the number of black squares and the number of white squares. If you've deleted
      two black squares, then you have 30 black squares and 32 white squares left. Now any
      domino can only cover 1 white and 1 black square. So 2 white squares **have** to be left
      uncovered.

Chapter 2
Answers for Exercises

1. $y = 6;\ x = 5$

2.   Three non-collinear points are needed to define a circle uniquely.

3.   Let $P(x, y)$ represent any point on the circle.
     Then $CP = r$.
     Using the distance formula (which is really just
     the Pythagorean Theorem) we get
     $$\sqrt{(x-a)^2 + (y-b)^2} = r^2.$$
     Squaring gives $(x-a)^2 + (y-b)^2 = r^2$ as the
     equation of the circle.

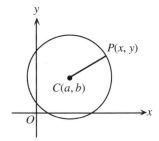

4.   The equation of OB is $y = 3x$ and the equation of the dotted line is $x = 3$. The midpoint
     of OB is $D\left(\dfrac{3}{2}, \dfrac{9}{2}\right)$. Since the slope of OB is 3, the slope of DC is $-\dfrac{1}{3}$. Hence the
     equation of DC is $y = -\dfrac{1}{3}x + 5$.
     Solving $y = -\dfrac{1}{3}x + 5$ with $x = 3$ gives the coordinates of the centre C as $(3, 4)$. So the
     radius OC is 5 and the equation of the circle is $(x-3)^2 + (y-4)^2 = 25$.

5. $(x-1)^2 + (y-2)^2 = 25$

6. $(x-1)^2 + (y-2)^2 = 9$

7.   (a) $(-3, 2), 5$ (b) $(4, -2), 5$

8.   The centre of the circle is $(5, -4)$ and the radius
     is 5.
     Hence the coordinates of B, the other end of the
     diameter from A, are $(9, -7)$.

     $\overline{A(1, -1) \qquad (5, -4) \qquad\qquad B}$

9.   (i) $7, -9$ (ii) $4, \dfrac{2}{3}$ (iii) $\dfrac{2}{3}, 4$ (iv) $\pm 3,\ \pm\sqrt{7}$
     (iv) $-\dfrac{1}{2}$ (vi) $-5, \dfrac{1}{5}$

10. (i) $x > 9$ or $x < -7$ (ii) $-4 \le x \le -\dfrac{2}{3}$

11. (i)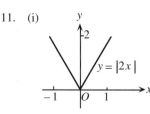

(ii)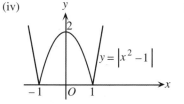

(iii)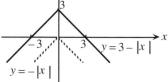

(iv)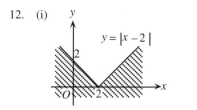

(v)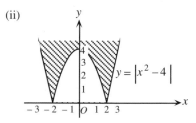

Hint: First sketch the graph of $y = -|x|$ (dotted), then translate this graph 3 units upward.

12. (i)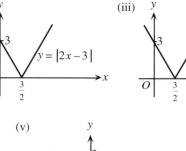

(ii)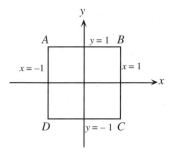

13.   To sketch the graph of $|y - x| + |y + x| = 2$ we consider four cases.

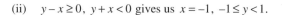

(i) $y - x \geq 0,\ y + x \geq 0$

This gives $(y - x) + (y + x) = 2$

$y = 1.$

But, to satisfy the original equation, we must also include the condition $-1 \leq x \leq 1$.

From these we get the line segment AB.

(ii) $y - x \geq 0,\ y + x < 0$ gives us $x = -1,\ -1 \leq y < 1$.

(iii) $y - x < 0,\ y + x \geq 0$ gives us $x = 1,\ -1 \leq y < 1$.

(iv) $y - x < 0,\ y + x < 0$ gives us $y = -1,\ -1 < x < 1$.

At last! A square that's nicely positioned.

Solutions to Problems

1. *Solution*

    In the diagram, the centre of the circle is $A(3, 4)$

    which is $\sqrt{3^2 + 4^2} = 5$ units from the origin.
    If OB is tangent to the circle from the origin, then
    $AB \perp OB$.
    Therefore, by the Pythagorean Theorem,

    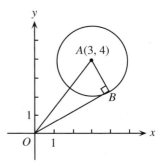

    $$OB = \sqrt{(OA)^2 - (AB)^2}$$
    $$= \sqrt{5^2 - 2^2}$$
    $$= \sqrt{21}.$$

    The length of the required tangent is $\sqrt{21}$.

2. *Solution*

    Since the areas are equal,

    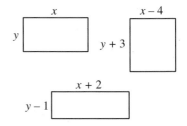

    $$xy = (x-4)(y+3) = (x+2)(y-1).$$
    Since $xy = (x-4)(y+3)$
    $$xy = xy + 3x - 4y - 12$$
    $$3x - 4y - 12 = 0 \qquad (1)$$
    Also, $xy = (x+2)(y-1)$
    $$xy = xy - x + 2y - 2$$
    $$x - 2y + 2 = 0 \qquad (2)$$
    Equation (1) minus $2 \times$ equation (2) gives $x = 16$.
    Substitute $x = 16$ in (2) to give $y = 9$.
    Therefore the area of each rectangle is $16 \times 9 = 144$.

3. *Solution*

    The coordinates of B are $(3, 3m+4)$.
    Since $OC \parallel AB$, the quadrilateral is a trapezoid.
    The area of trapezoid $OABC$ is

    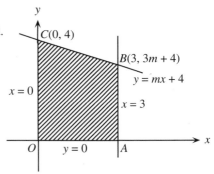

    $$\frac{1}{2}(AB + OC)(OA).$$

    Therefore $9 = \frac{1}{2}[(3m+4)+4](3)$

    $$18 = 9m + 24$$
    $$m = -\frac{2}{3}.$$

4. *Solution 1*

   $A(3, 7)$ and $B(-3, -5)$ are two points on the line.

   Slope $AB = \dfrac{-5-7}{-3-3} = \dfrac{-12}{-6} = 2.$

   Therefore the equation of the line is

   $$y - 7 = 2(x - 3) \text{ or } y = 2x + 1.$$

   Solution 2

   Let $f(x) = mx + b$.

   Therefore $f(3) = 3m + b = 7$

   and $f(-3) = -3m + b = -5$.

   Solving gives $m = 2, b = 1$.

   The equation of the line is $y = 2x + 1$.

5. *Solution*

   (a)

   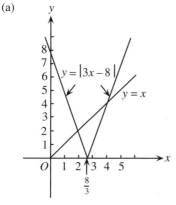

   (b) First we find the points of intersection of $y = x$ and $y = |3x - 8|$.

   If $3x - 8 \geq 0$, that is $x \geq \dfrac{8}{3}$, we have $x = 3x - 8$

   $$2x = 8$$
   $$x = 4.$$

   If $3x - 8 < 0$, that is, $x < \dfrac{8}{3}$, we have $x = -3x + 8$

   $$4x = 8$$
   $$x = 2.$$

   From the graph, the solution of the inequality $x > |3x - 8|$ is $2 < x < 4$.

6.   *Solution 1*
     Draw the graphs of $y = |x+3|$ and $y = 2|x-3|$.

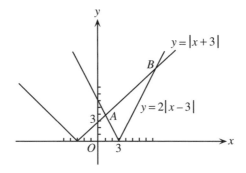

The graphs intersect in two places. At A we have

$$x+3 = -2(x-3)$$
$$3x = 3$$
$$x = 1.$$

At B we have

$$x+3 = -2(x-3)$$
$$x = 9.$$

Therefore the sum of all values of x for which $|x+3| = 2|x-3|$ is $1+9 = 10$.

Solution 2
$|x+3| = 2|x-3|$
If $x \geq 3$, $x+3 = 2(x-3)$
$$x = 9.$$
If $-3 \leq x \leq 3$, $x+3 = -2(x-3)$
$$x = 1.$$
If $x < -3$, $-(x+3) = -2(x-3)$
$$x = 9 \text{ which contradicts the fact that } x < -3.$$
Hence the sum of all values of x for which $|x+3| = 2|x-3|$ is $1+9 = 10$.

7.   *Solution*

The equation $(x-5)^2 + (y+12)^2 = 49$ represents a circle with centre $(5, -12)$ and radius 7.

The equation $x^2 + y^2 = k^2$ represents a circle with centre $(0, 0)$ and radius k.

If these circles touch at precisely one point, they are tangent circles, and the point of tangency is on the line connecting their centres. There are two possible circles with points of contact at P or at Q as in the diagram.

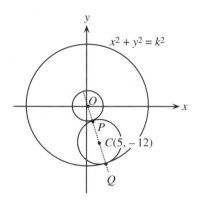

Since $OC = \sqrt{5^2 + (-12)^2} = 13$,

$\qquad k = OP = 13 - 7 = 6.$

or $\quad k = OQ = 13 + 7 = 20.$

Then $k = 6$ or 20.

8.   *Solution*

The point on the circle which is nearest to $A(-4, 3)$ is the point of intersection of the line joining A to the centre of the circle.

Join $A(-4, 3)$ to the origin to intersect the circle at P.

Drop perpendiculars AB and PQ to the x-axis.

Now $\triangle OPQ$ is similar to $\triangle OAB$.

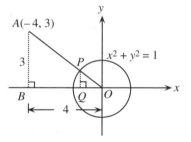

Hence $\dfrac{OQ}{OB} = \dfrac{QP}{BA} = \dfrac{OP}{OA}$

$\qquad \dfrac{OQ}{4} = \dfrac{QP}{3} = \dfrac{1}{5}.$

Thus $OQ = \dfrac{4}{5}$ and $QP = \dfrac{3}{5}$.

The point on the circle which is nearest to $(-4, 3)$ is $\left(-\dfrac{4}{5}, \dfrac{3}{5}\right)$.

Comment: I'll bet you didn't use this approach. You probably found the equation of the line through A and O and solved it with the circle equation. That's what I did, too; I thought that you might be interested in a different approach.

9.   (a)   *Solution*

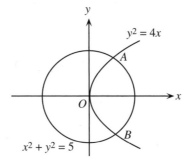

(b)   To find the coordinates of A and B, solve the equations of the circle and parabola.

Substitute $y^2 = 4x$ in $x^2 + y^2 = 5$.

$$x^2 + 4x = 5$$
$$x^2 + 4x - 5 = 0$$
$$(x + 5)(x - 1) = 0$$
$$x = -5 \quad \text{or} \quad x = 1.$$

For real x, $y^2 = 4x$ implies that $4x \geq 0$.

Therefore $x = 1$ is the only solution.

Substitution gives $y = \pm 2$.

The coordinates of A and B are $(1, 2)$ and $(1, -2)$, respectively.

The length of AB is 4.

10. *Solution*

(a)   To determine the coordinates of A and B substitute $y = 5x - 13$ in the circle equation to obtain

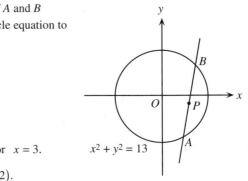

$$x^2 + (5x - 13)^2 = 13$$
$$26x^2 - 130x + 156 = 0$$
$$x^2 - 5x + 6 = 0$$
$$(x - 2)(x - 3) = 0$$
$$x = 2 \quad \text{or} \quad x = 3.$$

Hence A is $(2, -3)$ and B is $(3, 2)$.

The coordinates of the midpoint of AB are $\left(\frac{5}{2}, -\frac{1}{2}\right)$.

(b) Things don't always go as nicely as they did in part (a). Here, if you actually calculate the coordinates of A and B, there is a lot of work to do. However, remember that the x-coordinate of P is the average of the x-coordinates of A and B. Recall also that the sum of the roots of the quadratic equation $ax^2 + bx + c = 0$ is $-\frac{b}{a}$. Using these facts, the x-coordinate of P is $\frac{6}{5}$, and hence P is the point $\left(\frac{6}{5}, -\frac{3}{5}\right)$.

11. *Solution*

Let the coordinates of A be $(a, 0)$.

Since B is on the line $2x + y = 0$, its coordinates are of the form $(b, -2b)$.

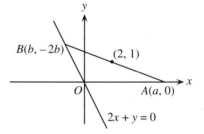

The midpoint of AB is $\left(\dfrac{a+b}{2}, \dfrac{0-2b}{2}\right) = (2, 1)$.

Hence, $\dfrac{a+b}{2} = 2$ (1)

and $\dfrac{-2b}{2} = 1$.   (2)

From (2), $b = -1$, and substituting into (1) gives $a = 5$.

Therefore the coordinates of A are $(5, 0)$.

12. *Solution*

Solving the line and circle equations, we obtain

$$(x - 2)^2 + (x - 2 - 1)^2 = 25$$
$$x^2 - 5x - 6 = 0$$
$$(x - 6)(x + 1) = 0.$$

Hence $x = -1$ gives point A to be $(-1, -3)$ and $x = 6$ gives point B to be $(6, 4)$.

Since $\angle ABC$ is a right angle, AC is the diameter.

Now the centre is $(2, 1)$, so C is $(2 + 3, 1 + 4) = (5, 5)$.

Then AB is $\sqrt{7^2 + 7^2} = 7\sqrt{2}$ and BC is $\sqrt{1^2 + 1^2} = \sqrt{2}$.

The area of $\triangle ABC$ is $\frac{1}{2}(7\sqrt{2})(\sqrt{2}) = 7$.

13. *Solution*

(a) Since B and C are on the y-axis, we set $x = 0$.

$$9 + y^2 = 25$$
$$y^2 = 16$$
$$y = \pm 4.$$

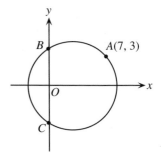

Then B is the point $(0, 4)$ and C is $(0, -4)$.

(b) We calculate BA, CA, and BC, obtaining

$$BA = \sqrt{7^2 + (3-4)^2} = \sqrt{50}$$
$$CA = \sqrt{7^2 + (3+4)^2} = \sqrt{98}$$
$$BC = 8.$$

Using the Law of Cosines,

$$\cos \angle BAC = \frac{50 + 98 - 64}{2\sqrt{50}\sqrt{98}} = \frac{3}{5}.$$

$$\angle BAC = \cos^{-1}\left(\frac{3}{5}\right) \quad \text{(approximately } 53°\text{)}.$$

14. *Solution*

(a) For the x-intercepts set $y = 0$. Then

$$2x^2 - x - 1 = 0$$
$$(2x + 1)(x - 1) = 0$$
$$x = -\frac{1}{2} \quad \text{or} \quad x = 1.$$

The x-intercepts are $-\frac{1}{2}$ and 1.

For the y-intercepts set $x = 0$. Then

$$y = \frac{0 - 0 - 1}{0 - 0 - 3} = \frac{1}{3}.$$

The y-intercept is $\frac{1}{3}$.

(b) Factoring numerator and denominator we get

$$y = \frac{(2x + 1)(x - 1)}{(x - 3)(x + 1)}.$$

The vertical asymptotes are $x = 3$ and $x = -1$.

(c)   For horizontal asymptotes we consider

$$\lim_{x \to \infty} \frac{2x^2 - x - 1}{x^2 - 2x - 3} = \lim_{x \to \infty} \frac{2 - \dfrac{1}{x} - \dfrac{1}{x^2}}{1 - \dfrac{2}{x} - \dfrac{3}{x^2}} = 2$$

and $$\lim_{x \to -\infty} \frac{2x^2 - x - 1}{x^2 - 2x - 3} = \lim_{x \to -\infty} \frac{2 - \dfrac{1}{x} - \dfrac{1}{x^2}}{1 - \dfrac{2}{x} - \dfrac{3}{x^2}} = 2.$$

There is one horizontal asymptote, $y = 2$.

(d)   For intersections of the curve and the horizontal asymptote, set $y = 2$ and obtain

$$2 = \frac{2x^2 - x - 1}{x^2 - 2x - 3}$$
$$2x^2 - 4x - 6 = 2x^2 - x - 1$$
$$3x = -5$$
$$x = -\frac{5}{3}.$$

There is one point of intersection, namely, $\left(-\frac{5}{3}, 2\right)$.

15.   *Solution 1*

Let Q be the point of contact of the tangent from the origin.

Since the centre of the circle is $C(5, 7)$ and its radius is 5, then the y-axis is also tangent with point of contact $P(0, 7)$.

Since OP and OQ are tangents from an external point, then $OP = OQ = 7$.

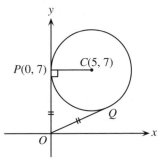

Solution 2

The centre of the circle is $C(5, 7)$ and the radius is 5.

Now, $OC = \sqrt{5^2 + 7^2}$

$$= \sqrt{74}.$$

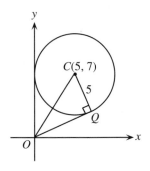

Let Q be a point of contact of the tangent with the circle.

Since $OQ \perp CQ$ (radius $\perp$ tangent), then, by the Pythagorean Theorem,

$$OQ = \sqrt{(OC)^2 - (CQ)^2}$$

$$= \sqrt{74 - 25}$$

$$= 7.$$

Therefore the distance from the origin to the point of contact of the tangent is 7.

16. *Solution 1*

The equation $f(x) + k = 0$ or $f(x) = -k$ will have four different roots if its curve intersects the horizontal line, defined by $y = -k$, in four distinct points.

This will occur if $-2 < -k < -1$, that is, if $1 < k < 2$.

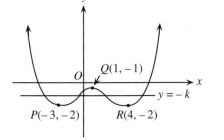

Solution 2

The equation $f(x) + k = 0$ will have four different roots it the x-axis intersects the curve $y = f(x) + k$ in four distinct points.

This will occur if the given curve is translated upwards more than 1 unit but less than 2 units.

Hence $1 < k < 2$.

17. *Solution*

To sketch the graph of $|y-x|+|x|=2$ we consider four cases.

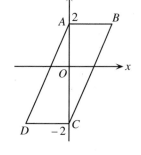

(i) $y-x \geq 0$, $x \geq 0$

This gives $(y-x)+x = 2$

$$y = 2.$$

But, to satisfy the original equation, we must also include the condition $0 \leq x \leq 2$.

From these we get line segment AB.

(ii) Similarly, $y-x < 0$, $x \geq 0$ gives us $y = 2x - 2$, with the added condition $0 \leq x < 2$. These give us line segment BC.

(iii) $y-x \geq 0$, $x < 0$ gives us $y = 2x + 2$ with the added condition $-2 \leq x < 0$.

These give us line segment AD.

(iv) $y-x < 0$, $x < 0$ gives us $y = -2$ with the added condition $-2 < x < 0$.

These give us line segment DC.

Thus the graph of $|y-x|+|x|=2$ is the parallelogram $ABCD$.

Chapter 3
Answers for Exercises

1. Maybe he was just lucky. For some reason I don't understand, just recently I got a laugh from a class when I added the numbers 1 to 6 in the following way, noted in the diagram. So three sevens are 21.

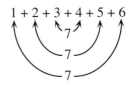

2. There's a lot to find out about the boy from Braunschweig, Germany. Look up a history of mathematics in the library.

3. Kirkman is less famous. He was an English minister in the 19th Century with an interest in mathematics. You might find his schoolgirl problem in a book on discrete math or combinatorics.

4. Appel and Haken proved the Four Colour Theorem in 1977.

5. Evariste Galois threw the duster at an examiner because he thought the examiner was being thick. Incidentally, Evariste failed the exam. (Is that surprising?) But he did make a big contribution to showing that, unlike the quadratic equation, a general quintic equation (one with an x^5 term) cannot be solved by a formula.

   Unfortunately Evariste was wounded in the duel and died of peritonitis. He did, however, have a whole area of abstract algebra, Galois Theory, named after him. I'm not sure how much consolation that was.

6. 10 050   7. 1 500 500   8. (a) 5700   (b) 1458

9. No. All is well. If n is even, then the 2 divides into the n. If n is odd, then $n-1$ is even and so is the square bracket $[2a+(n-1)d]$.

10. Why not? Where in the text did we need a or d to be integers? Of course, we need n to be an integer though.

11. (a) 1015   (b) 20, 30

12. If $r=1$, we are dividing by zero which is absolutely forbidden. The way I wrote the formula it looks as if $1-r$ has to be positive. However, $S_n = \dfrac{a\left(1-r^n\right)}{1-r} = \dfrac{a\left(r^n-1\right)}{r-1}$.

   So r **can** be bigger than 1. (We don't actually have to rewrite the formula.)

13. (a) $3\left(2^{10}-1\right)$ (b) $1-\left(\frac{1}{2}\right)^{n}$

14. The sequence $a, a, a, \ldots a$ is both an AP and a GP.

15. Use $n^{4}-(n-1)^{4}=4n^{3}-6n^{2}+4n-1$, then sum up all such equations down to

$1^{4}-0^{4}=4.1^{3}-6.1^{2}+4.1-1$. You should find that $1^{3}+2^{3}+3^{3}+\ldots+n^{3}=\dfrac{n^{2}}{4}(n+1)^{2}$.

Isn't that a surprise!

16. $\dfrac{2}{3}n(n+1)(2n+1)$.

Solutions to Problems

1. *Solution 1*

If t_n is the nth term of an arithmetic sequence, then $t_n = a + (n-1)d$

$$1994 = -1994 + n(n-1)2$$
$$2n = 3990$$
$$n = 1995.$$

Therefore there are 1995 terms.

Solution 2

The sequence contains the terms $0, \pm 2, \pm 4, \ldots, \pm 1994$.

There are $2(997)+1=1995$ terms.

2. *Solution*

The first few terms are $5, 3, -2, -5, -3, 2, 5, 3, -2, -5 \ldots$.

The sequence repeats every six terms and since the sum of the first six terms is 0, then the sum of the first 32 terms is $5(0)+5+3=8$.

3. *Solution*

$$\sin\left(\frac{\pi}{6}\right)+\sin^{2}\left(\frac{\pi}{6}\right)+\sin^{3}\left(\frac{\pi}{6}\right)+\ldots=\frac{1}{2}+\left(\frac{1}{2}\right)^{2}+\left(\frac{1}{2}\right)^{3}+\ldots$$
$$=\frac{\frac{1}{2}}{1-\frac{1}{2}}$$
$$=1.$$

4.   *Solution 1*
      The first and last terms of the sequence that are between 40 and 28 001 are 42 and
      28 000, respectively.

      Therefore the number of terms between 40 and 28 001 is $\frac{28\,000 - 42}{7} + 1 = 3995$.

      Solution 2
      The first and last terms of the sequence that are between 40 and 28 001 are 42 and
      28 000, respectively.
      Let n be the number of terms in the sequence.
      Using the formula $t_n = a + (n-1)d$ gives

      $$28\,000 = 42 + (n-1)7$$
      $$28\,000 = 42 + 7n - 7$$
      $$7n = 27\,965$$
      $$n = 3995.$$

      There are 3995 terms between 40 and 28 001.

      Solution 3
      The given sequence can be expressed as 7, 14, 21, ..., $7n$, ...
      Hence, $40 < 7n < 28\,001$

      $$42 \le 7n \le 28\,000$$
      $$6 \le n \le 4000.$$

      There are $4000 - 6 + 1 = 3995$ terms between 40 and 28 001.

5.   *Solution 1*
      We are given $f(n+1) = \dfrac{3f(n)+1}{3}$, $n = 1, 2, 3, \dots$.

      Rewrite this as $f(n+1) - f(n) = \dfrac{1}{3}$.

      Since the difference between successive terms is constant, the terms $f(1), f(2), f(3), \dots$

      form an arithmetic sequence with $a = f(1) = 2$ and common difference $d = \dfrac{1}{3}$.

      Using the fact that $t_n = a + (n-1)d$, we get

      $$f(100) = 2 + 99\left(\frac{1}{3}\right)$$
      $$= 35.$$

Solution 2

$$f(n+1) - f(n) = \frac{1}{3}$$

$$f(n) - f(n-1) = \frac{1}{3}$$

$$f(n-1) - f(n-2) = \frac{1}{3}$$

. . .

$$f(3) - f(2) = \frac{1}{3}$$

$$f(2) - f(1) = \frac{1}{3}$$

Adding: $f(n+1) = f(1) + n\left(\frac{1}{3}\right)$.

If $n = 99$, we get $f(100) = 2 + 33 = 35$.

6. *Solution*

The arithmetic sequence that is formed is 120, 125, 130, 135, ..., $120 + 5(n-1)$.

The corresponding exterior angles will be 60, 55, 50, ..., $(65 - 5n)$.

Since the sum of the exterior angles of a polygon is $360°$, $\frac{n}{2}[60 + (65 - 5n)] = 360°$.

$$n(125 - 5n) = 720$$

$$5n^2 - 125n + 720 = 0$$

$$n^2 - 25n + 144 = 0$$

$$(n-16)(n-9) = 0$$

$$n = 16 \quad \text{or} \quad n = 9.$$

If $n = 16$ the nth exterior angle becomes $65 - 5(16) = -20$ which is not possible. Therefore the polygon has 9 sides.

7. *Solution 1*

Four terms forming a geometric sequence are of the form a, ar, ar^2, ar^3.

Since $a = 27$, the four terms become $27, 27r, 27r^2, 27r^3$.

But $27r^3 = 8$

$$r^3 = \frac{8}{27}$$

$$r = \frac{2}{3}.$$

$$x = 27r = 27\left(\frac{2}{3}\right) = 18.$$

$$y = 27r^2 = 27\left(\frac{4}{9}\right) = 12.$$

Thus $x = 18$ and $y = 12$.

Solution 2

Since the sequence is geometric, the ratio of successive pairs of terms must be equal.

Hence $\dfrac{x}{27} = \dfrac{y}{x} = \dfrac{8}{y}$.

From there we get $8x = y^2$ (1)

and $xy = (8)(27)$ (2)

From (1), $8xy = y^3$

$$y^3 = (8)(8)(27)$$

$$y = 2.2.3 = 12.$$

Substitute in (1) to give $x = 18$.

Thus $x = 18$ and $y = 12$.

8.   *Solution*

Simplifying $2^1 \cdot 2^2 \cdot 2^3 \cdot .... \cdot 2^n = 2^{210}$ we get

$$2^{1+2+3+...+n} = 2^{210}.$$

Therefore $1 + 2 + 3 + ... + n = 210$.

Then $\dfrac{n(n+1)}{2} = 210$

$$n^2 + n - 420 = 0$$

$$(n - 20)(n + 21) = 0$$

$$n = 20 \ \text{ or } \ -21.$$

Since n is a positive integer, $n = -21$ is inadmissible.

Therefore $n = 20$.

9.   *Solution 1*

The average of the 25 integers is $\dfrac{500}{25} = 20$.

Since the 25 integers are consecutive, 20 is the 13th term of the sequence.

Therefore the smallest of the 25 integers is $20 - 13 + 1 = 8$.

Solution 2

Let the sequence be $x, \ x+1, \ x+2, ..., \ x+24$.

Therefore, $x + (x+1) + (x+2) + \cdots + (x+24) = 500$

$$25x + 300 = 500$$

$$25x = 200$$

$$x = 8.$$

The smallest integer in the sequence is 8.

10.   *Solution 1*

Since the line $px + qy = r$ passes through the point $(-1, 2)$, then $-p + 2q = r$.

Thus $q - p = r - q$, and hence p, q, and r are consecutive terms of an arithmetic sequence, since the differences between consecutive terms are equal.

Solution 2

Since the line $px + qy = r$ passes through the point $(-1, 2)$, then $-p + 2q = r$.

Hence $2q = p + r$ or $q = \dfrac{p + r}{2}$.

Thus q is the arithmetic mean of p and r, so p, q, and r are consecutive terms of an arithmetic sequence.

11. *Solution*

  (i)   We are given $S_n = 3^n - 1$, where n is a positive integer.

       Therefore $S_1 = 3^1 - 1 = 2$, $S_2 = 3^2 - 1 = 8$, and $S_3 = 3^3 - 1 = 26$.

       Since $t_n = S_n - S_{n-1}$ for $n > 1$.

$$t_1 = S_1 = 2,$$
$$t_2 = S_2 - S_1 = 8 - 2 = 6,$$
$$t_3 = S_3 - S_2 = 26 - 8 = 18.$$

  (ii)   *Solution 1*

       For $n = 1$, $\dfrac{t_2}{t_1} = \dfrac{6}{2} = 3$.

       For $n > 1$, $\dfrac{t_{n+1}}{t_n} = \dfrac{S_{n+1} - S_n}{S_n - S_{n-1}}$

$$= \frac{3^{n+1} - 1 - \left(3^n - 1\right)}{3^n - 1 - \left(3^{n-1} - 1\right)}$$

$$= \frac{3^{n+1} - 3^n}{3^n - 3^{n-1}}$$

$$= \frac{3\left(3^n - 3^{n-1}\right)}{3^n - 3^{n-1}}$$

$$= 3.$$

Therefore for all values of n, $\dfrac{t_{n+1}}{t_n} = 3$ and so $\dfrac{t_{n+1}}{t_n}$ is constant.

Solution 2

For $n=1$, $\dfrac{t_2}{t_1} = \dfrac{6}{2} = 3$.

For $n>1$, $t_n = S_n - S_{n-1}$

$$= 3^n - 1 - \left(3^{n-1} - 1\right)$$

$$= 3 \cdot 3^{n-1} - 3^{n-1}$$

$$= 2 \cdot 3^{n-1}.$$

Hence $t_{n+1} = 2 \cdot 3^n$.

Therefore $\dfrac{t_{n+1}}{t_n} = \dfrac{2 \cdot 3^n}{2 \cdot 3^{n-1}} = 3$, and so, for all values of n, $\dfrac{t_{n+1}}{t_n}$ is constant.

12. *Solution*

Since the sum of the first n odd integers is n^2, then the sum of $1+3+5+ ... + p$ which

has $\dfrac{p+1}{2}$ terms is $\left(\dfrac{p+1}{2}\right)^2$.

Similarly, $1+3+5+...+q = \left(\dfrac{q+1}{2}\right)^2$ and $1+3+5+...+19 = \left(\dfrac{19+1}{2}\right)^2 = 100$.

Therefore the given equation becomes $\left(\dfrac{p+1}{2}\right)^2 + \left(\dfrac{q+1}{2}\right)^2 = 100$.

The only two positive integers whose squares have a sum of 100 are 6 and 8.

Assuming $p<q$, $\dfrac{p+1}{2} = 6$ and so $p=11$, and $\dfrac{q+1}{2} = 8$ and so $q=15$.

Therefore $p+q = 11+15 = 26$.

13. *Solution*

Since $1+3+3^2 + \cdots + 3^n$ is a geometric series, then $p = \dfrac{3^{n+1}-1}{2}$.

The sum of the integers from 1 to p is $1+2+3+\cdots+p = \dfrac{p(p+1)}{2}$

$$= \dfrac{1}{2}\left(\dfrac{3^{n+1}-1}{2}\right)\left(\dfrac{3^{n+1}-1}{2}+1\right)$$

$$= \dfrac{1}{2}\left(\dfrac{3^{n+1}-1}{2}\right)\left(\dfrac{3^{n+1}+1}{2}\right)$$

$$= \dfrac{9^{n+1}-1}{8}.$$

Also $1 + 9 + 9^2 + \cdots + 9^n = \dfrac{9^{n+1} - 1}{8}$.

Hence the sum of the integers from 1 to p is $\left(1 + 9 + 9^2 + \cdots + 9^n\right)$.

14. *Solution*

(a) The area of the figure is given by

$$A = 1 + s^2 + s^4 + s^6 + \cdots = \dfrac{1}{1 - s^2}.$$

[This is an infinite geometric sum with $a = 1$, $r = s^2$ and with $0 < s^2 < 1$.]

(b) Note that the sum of the small vertical pieces is 1 and that the sum of the horizontal pieces is $1 + s + s^2 + \cdots$ for both the top and the bottom.

The perimeter is given by

$$P = 2 + 2\left(1 + s + s^2 + s^3 + \cdots\right)$$

$$= 2 + 2\left(\dfrac{1}{1 - s}\right)$$

$$= \dfrac{4 - 2s}{1 - s}.$$

(c) $\dfrac{A}{P} = \dfrac{\dfrac{1}{1 - s^2}}{\dfrac{4 - 2s}{1 - s}}$

$$= \dfrac{1}{(1 - s)(1 + s)} \cdot \dfrac{1 - s}{4 - 2s}$$

$$= \dfrac{1}{(1 + s)(4 - 2s)}. \qquad (\text{since } s \neq 1)$$

Hence $\dfrac{1}{(1 + s)(4 - 2s)} = \dfrac{8}{35}$

$$16s^2 - 16s + 3 = 0$$

$$(4s - 1)(4s - 3) = 0$$

$$s = \dfrac{1}{4} \quad \text{or} \quad s = \dfrac{3}{4}.$$

There are precisely two acceptable values for s.

15. *Solution 1*

The expression is the sum of the squares of the odd integers, or the sum of the squares of $(2n-1)$ integers less the sum of the squares of the even integers. Now

$$1^2 + 2^2 + 3^2 + \cdots + k^2 = \frac{k(k+1)(2k+1)}{6}.$$

Therefore $1^2 + 2^2 + 3^2 + \cdots + (2n-1)^2 = \dfrac{(2n-1)(2n)(4n-1)}{6}$

and $2^2 + 4^2 + 6^2 + \cdots + (2n-2)^2 = 4\left[1^2 + 2^2 + 3^2 + \cdots + (n-1)^2\right]$

$$= 4\frac{(n-1)(n)(2n-1)}{6}.$$

Hence $1^2 + 3^2 + 5^2 + \cdots + (2n-1)^2 = \dfrac{(2n-1)(2n)(4n-1)}{6} - \dfrac{4(n-1)(n)(2n-1)}{6}$

$$= \frac{2n(2n-1)\left[4n-1-2(n-1)\right]}{6}$$

$$= \frac{2n(2n-1)(2n+1)}{6}$$

$$= \frac{4n^3 - n}{3}$$

$$= n^3 + \frac{n^3 - n}{3}$$

$$\geq n^3. \qquad \left(\text{since } \frac{n^3 - n}{3} \geq 0 \text{ for } n \geq 1.\right)$$

Solution 2

We shall use mathematical induction.

For $n = 1$, equality holds and for $n = 2$ the inequality is true.

Assume that the result is true for $n = k$; that is, $1^2 + 3^2 + 5^2 + \cdots + (2k-1)^2 \geq k^3$.

Then for $n = k+1$,

$$1^2 + 3^2 + 5^2 + \cdots + (2k-1)^2 + (2k+1)^2 \geq k^3 + (2k+1)^2$$

$$= k^3 + 4k^2 + 4k + 1$$

$$= (k+1)^3 + \left(k^2 + k\right)$$

$$\geq (k+1)^3,$$

since $k^2 + k > 0$ for $k > 1$.

Thus if the result is true for $n = k$, it is true for $n = k + 1$.

Since the result is true for $n = 1, 2$, by the principle of mathematical induction it is true for all natural numbers.

16. *Solution 1*

Let the first series be represented by $a_1 + (a_1 + d) + (a_1 + 2d) + \cdots + [a_1 + (n-1)d]$ where

the nth term is $t_n = a + (n-1)d$ and the sum of n terms is $S_n = \frac{n}{2}[2a + (n-1)d]$.

Represent the second series by $a_2 + (a_2 + l) + (a_2 + 2l) + \cdots + [a_2 + (n-1)l]$ where the

nth term is $T_n = a_2 + (n-1)l$ and the sum of n terms is $R_n = \frac{n}{2}[2a_2 + (n-1)l]$.

We would like to determine $\dfrac{t_{11}}{T_{11}} = \dfrac{a_1 + 10d}{a_2 + 10l}$.

Now $\dfrac{S_n}{R_n} = \dfrac{\frac{n}{2}[2a_1 + (n-1)d]}{\frac{n}{2}[2a_2 + (n-1)l]}$

$= \dfrac{2a_1 + (n-1)d}{2a_2 + (n-1)l}$.

Dividing the numerator and denominator by 2 will give

$\dfrac{S_n}{R_n} = \dfrac{a_1 + \dfrac{n-1}{2}d}{a_2 + \dfrac{n-1}{2}l}$.

If $\dfrac{n-1}{2} = 10$, $n = 21$ and so $\dfrac{S_{21}}{R_{21}} = \dfrac{t_{11}}{T_{11}}$.

But $\dfrac{S_n}{R_n} = \dfrac{7n+1}{4n+27}$.

Therefore $\dfrac{S_{21}}{R_{21}} = \dfrac{7(21)+1}{4(21)+27}$

$= \dfrac{148}{111}$

$= \dfrac{4}{3}$

$= \dfrac{t_{11}}{T_{11}}$.

The ratio of their eleventh terms is 4:3.

17. *Solution*

Letting the four parts be a, $a+d$, $a+2d$, and $a+3d$ will lead to equations which are difficult to solve. If, instead, we let the four parts be $a-3d$, $a-d$, $a+d$, and $a+3d$, the algebra will be much simpler.

Now $(a-3d)+(a-d)+(a+d)+(a+3d)=1$.

$$4a = 1$$

$$a = \frac{1}{4}.$$

Also $(a-3d)^3 + (a-d)^3 + (a+d)^3 + (a+3d)^3 = \frac{1}{10}$.

Cubing the terms on the left side and simplifying, we get

$$4a^3 + 60ad^2 = \frac{1}{10}.$$

Substitute $a = \frac{1}{4}$ to give $\frac{1}{16} + 15d^2 = \frac{1}{10}$

$$15d^2 = \frac{3}{80}$$

$$d^2 = \frac{1}{400}$$

$$d = \pm\frac{1}{20}.$$

The four parts are $\frac{1}{20}, \frac{1}{5}, \frac{3}{10}, \frac{2}{5}$.

Using $d = -\frac{1}{20}$ produces the same four numbers in reverse order.

Chapter 4
Answers for Exercises

1. I know that Peter can do this room in 2 hours, while Sue takes 3 hours. So does Sue take one and a half times longer to paint this room? Does that mean that $s = \frac{3}{2}p$ or $s = \frac{2}{3}p$? Or is there some other relation between s and p?

2. Well, we'd still have $p + s = 1$, but I guess that now $s = \frac{4}{5}p$ or else $s = \frac{5}{4}p$. So we haven't gotten ahead by much. We might think about painting nine roons. Now Peter could paint four of them in 20 hours and Sue could paint five of them in the same time. Could you convert that to one room? Where does the nine come from, I wonder?

3. (i) $p = \frac{3}{5}, \ s = \frac{2}{5}$ (ii) $p = \frac{2}{5}, \ s = \frac{3}{5}$.

4. If $a < 0$, then the graphs of Figure 1 are turned upside down. If $a = 0$, then we don't have a quadratic.

5. This is a much more difficult problem

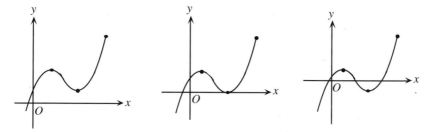

A cubic can have one, two or three roots as I've shown in the diagram. (Here $a > 0$. If $a < 0$, we just tip everything upside down as with the quadratic.)

To actually say when we get each of these cases is difficult. Although there is a formula for solving $ax^3 + bx^2 + cx + d = 0$, it is rather complicated.

6. $r_1 + r_2 + r_3 + r_4 = -\frac{b}{a}; \ r_1 r_2 + r_1 r_3 + r_1 r_4 + r_2 r_3 + r_2 + r_4 + r_3 r_4 = \frac{c}{a};$

    $r_1 r_2 r_3 + r_1 r_2 r_4 + r_1 r_3 r_4 = -\frac{d}{a}; \ r_1 r_2 r_3 r_4 = \frac{e}{a}.$

7. This can get length to write. Let's just express it in summation notation. The sum of the roots $\sum r_i = -\frac{b}{a}$; the sum of product pairs $\sum r_i r_j = \frac{c}{a}$; the sum of product triples $\sum r_i r_j r_k r_l = -\frac{d}{a}$; the sum of product quadruples $\sum r_i r_j r_k r_l = \frac{e}{a}$; the product of the roots $r_1 r_2 r_3 r_4 r_5 = -\frac{f}{a}$.

8. (i) $x^2 + x - 30 = (x+6)(x-5)$. Hence the roots are -6 and 5.

    (ii) $x^3 + 2x^2 - x - 2 = (x+2)(x^2 - 1) = (x+2)(x-1)(x+1)$. Hence the roots are -2, -1, 1;

    (iii) $4x^4 - 1 = (2x^2 - 1)(2x^2 + 1) = (\sqrt{2}x - 1)(\sqrt{2}x + 1)(2x^2 + 1)$. Since $2x^2 + 1 > 0$ for all x, the only real roots here are $\frac{1}{\sqrt{2}}, \frac{1}{\sqrt{2}}$;

    (iv) $3x^4 - 22x^3 + 57x^2 - 62x + 24 = (3x-4)(x-1)(x-2)(x-3)$. The roots are 1, $\frac{4}{3}$, 2 and 3.

9.

	x_0	x_1	x_2	x_3	x_4	x_5
$2.5x(1-x)$	0.1	0.225	0.43594	0.61474	0.59209	0.60380
	0.5	0.625	0.58594	0.60654	0.59662	0.60166
$3.1x(1-x)$	0.1	0.279	0.62359	0.72765	0.61435	0.73447
	0.2	0.496	0.77495	0.54065	0.76988	0.54921
$4x(1-x)$	0.2	0.64	0.9216	0.28901	0.82194	0.58420
	0.21	0.6636	0.89294	0.38239	0.94467	0.20906
$2x(1-x)$	0.5	0.5	0.5	0.5	0.5	0.5

10. $x = 0$ or $\frac{\lambda - 1}{\lambda}$.

11. Let $f(f(x)) = x$.

    Then $\lambda^2 x(1-x)(1 - \lambda x + \lambda x^2) = x$, so $x\left[\lambda^2(1-x)(1 - \lambda x + \lambda x^2) - 1\right] = 0$.

    Now $\lambda^2(1-x)(1 - \lambda x + \lambda x^2) - 1 = -\lambda^3 x^3 + 2\lambda^3 x^2 - x(\lambda^3 + \lambda^2) + \lambda^2 - 1$

    $\qquad = -\left[\lambda^3 x^3 - 2\lambda^3 x^2 + (\lambda^3 + \lambda^2)x - \lambda^2 + 1\right]$

    $\qquad = -\left[\lambda x - (\lambda - 1)\right]\left[\lambda^2 x^2 - (\lambda^2 + \lambda)x + \lambda + 1\right]$.

So $f(f(x)) = x$ when $x = 0$, $\dfrac{\lambda - 1}{\lambda}$ or when $\lambda^2 x^2 - (\lambda^2 + \lambda)x + (\lambda + 1) = 0$. The first two points are fixed points. As such they are not genuine period 2 points. Let's solve the quadratic to give the period 2 points. Here

$$x = \frac{(\lambda^2 + \lambda) \pm \sqrt{(\lambda^2 + \lambda)^2 - 4\lambda^2(\lambda + 1)}}{2\lambda^2}$$

$$= \frac{(\lambda^2 + \lambda) \pm \sqrt{\lambda^4 + 2\lambda^3 + \lambda^2 - 4\lambda^3 - 4\lambda^2}}{2\lambda^2}$$

$$= \frac{(\lambda^2 + \lambda) \pm \sqrt{\lambda^4 - 2\lambda^3 - 3\lambda^2}}{2\lambda^2}$$

$$= \frac{(\lambda + 1) \pm \sqrt{\lambda^2 - 2\lambda - 3}}{2\lambda^2}.$$

There are two period 2 points provided this discriminant is not negative. This means $\lambda^2 - 2\lambda - 3 \geq 0$.

But $\lambda^2 - 2\lambda - 3 = (\lambda - 3)(\lambda + 1)$. Hence $\lambda^2 - 2\lambda - 3 \geq 0$, provided $\lambda \geq 3$ or $\lambda \leq -1$.

When $\lambda = 3.1$ the period 2 points are $\dfrac{4.1 \pm \sqrt{0.41}}{6.2} = 0.76457$ or 0.57766. This is not inconsistent with the values found in Exercise 9. However, many more iterations would be required to get near to the values we have just given.

Solutions to Problems

1.   *Solution*

$x^2 - y^2 = 21$ (1)

$x - y = 3$ (2)

From (2), $x = 3 + y$ (3)

Substitute (3) into (1): $(3 + y)^2 - y^2 = 21$

$$9 + 6y + y^2 - y^2 = 21$$

$$6y = 12$$

$$y = 2.$$

Substitute $y = 2$ in (2) to get $x = 5$.

Therefore $x = 5$ and $y = 2$.

2. *Solution*

    Since $x = -2$ is a solution of the equation $x^3 - 7x - 6 = 0$, then $x + 2$ is a factor of $x^3 - 7x - 6$.

    Hence $x^3 - 7x - 6 = (x + 2)p(x)$.

    We obtain $p(x)$ by long division, synthetic division, or by inspection.

    [You can certainly do the long division. If you don't know synthetic division, ask your teacher. I prefer inspection, because it takes little space and is a good intellectual exercise.]

    By inspection $p(x)$ is of the form $x^2 + bx - 3$. [Why?]

    If $x^3 - 7x - 6 = (x + 2)(x^2 + bx - 3)$

    $$= x^3 + (b + 2)x^2 + (2b - 3)x - 6, \text{ then } b = -2.$$

    Now $p(x) = x^2 - 2x - 3 = (x - 3)(x + 1)$.

    If $(x + 2)(x - 3)(x + 1) = 0$, then $x = -2$ or 3 or -1.

    The other roots are 3 and -1.

3. *Solution 1*

    [Note that by combining equations (1) and (3) we can eliminate both x and y.]

    $$x + 2y - 3z = -1 \quad (1)$$
    $$2x + 5y + 12z = 9 \quad (2)$$
    $$3x + 6y - 3z = 1 \quad (3)$$

    (1) $\times 3$: $3x + 6y - 9z = -3$ (4)

    (3) $-$ (4): $6z = 4$

    $$z = \frac{2}{3}$$

    Set $z = \frac{2}{3}$ in (1): $x + 2y = 1$ (5)

    Set $z = \frac{2}{3}$ in (2): $2x + 5y = 1$ (6)

    (5) $\times 2$: $2x + 4y = 2$ (7)

    (6) $-$ (7): $y = -1$

    Then $x = 3$.

    There is only one solution, $(x, y, z) = \left(3, -1, \frac{2}{3}\right)$.

    Solution 2

    Using the augmented matrix form,

    $$\begin{bmatrix} 1 & 2 & -3 & -1 \\ 2 & 5 & 12 & 9 \\ 3 & 6 & -3 & 1 \end{bmatrix} \quad \sim \quad \begin{matrix} \\ R_2 - 2R_1 \\ R_3 - 3R_1 \end{matrix} \quad \begin{bmatrix} 1 & 2 & -3 & -1 \\ 0 & 1 & 18 & 11 \\ 0 & 0 & 6 & 4 \end{bmatrix}$$

$$\begin{array}{c} R_1 + \frac{1}{2}R_3 \\ R_2 - 3R_3 \\ \sim \end{array} \begin{bmatrix} 1 & 2 & 0 & 1 \\ 0 & 1 & 0 & -1 \\ 0 & 0 & 6 & 4 \end{bmatrix}$$

$$\begin{array}{c} R_1 - 2R_2 \\ \sim \\ \frac{1}{6}R_3 \end{array} \begin{bmatrix} 1 & 0 & 0 & 3 \\ 0 & 1 & 0 & -1 \\ 0 & 0 & 1 & \frac{2}{3} \end{bmatrix}$$

There is one solution, namely $(x, y, z) = \left(3, -1, \frac{2}{3}\right)$.

4. *Solution*

Since $\dfrac{a_m}{a_n} = \dfrac{m}{n}$, then $\dfrac{a_3}{a_{20}} = \dfrac{3}{20}$.

Hence, $\dfrac{5}{a_{20}} = \dfrac{3}{20}$

$$a_{20} = \frac{100}{3}.$$

5. *Solution*

$$x^2 + xy = 3 \qquad (1)$$
$$3x^2 + 2xy - 2y^2 = 7 \qquad (2)$$

Multiply equation (1) by 7 and equation (2) by 3:

$$7x^2 + 7xy = 21 \quad (3)$$
$$9x^2 + 6xy - 6y^2 = 21 \quad (4)$$

$(4) - (3):$ $\quad 2x^2 - xy - 6y^2 = 0$

$$(2x + 3y)(x - 2y) = 0$$

Then $x = -\dfrac{3}{2}y$ or $x = 2y$.

Substitute $x = -\dfrac{3}{2}y$ in equation (1):

$$\frac{9}{4}y^2 - \frac{3}{2}y^2 = 3$$

$$\frac{3}{4}y^2 = 3$$

$$y^2 = 4$$

$$y = \pm 2$$

and $\qquad x = \mp 3.$

Substitute $x = 2y$ in equation (1):

$$4y^2 + 2y^2 = 3$$

$$6y^2 = 3$$

$$y^2 = \frac{1}{2}$$

$$y = \pm \frac{1}{\sqrt{2}}$$

and $\qquad x = \pm\sqrt{2}.$

There are four solutions: $(x, y) = (-3, 2), (3, -2), \left(\sqrt{2}, \dfrac{1}{\sqrt{2}}\right), \left(-\sqrt{2}, -\dfrac{1}{\sqrt{2}}\right).$

[Don't forget to check that solutions satisfy the given equations.]

6.   *Solution*

$7x - 4y + 8z = 37$ (1)

$3x + 2y - 4z = 1$ (2)

$x^2 + y^2 + z^2 = 14$ (3)

$2 \times$ (2): $6x + 4y - 8z = 2$

adding: $13x = 39$

                 $x = 3.$

Substitute $x = 3$ in (2): $9 + 2y - 4z = 1$

                        $y = 2z - 4.$

Substitute $x = 3$ and $y = 2z - 4$ in (3)

$$9 + (2z - 4)^2 + z^2 = 14$$

$$5z^2 - 16z + 11 = 0$$

$$(z - 1)(5z - 11) = 0$$

$$z = 1 \text{ or } z = \frac{11}{5}.$$

Then $y = -2$ or $y = \dfrac{2}{5}.$

The solutions are $x = 3$, $y = -2$, $z = 1$, and $x = 3$, $y = \dfrac{2}{5}$, $z = \dfrac{11}{5}.$

7.   *Solution*

If the graph of the parabola $y = x^2 + mx + 16$ is always above the x-axis, then the graph has no real x-intercepts.

Hence the equation $x^2 + mx + 16 = 0$ has no real roots, and so the discriminant is negative.

Therefore, $m^2 - 4(16) < 0$

$$m^2 < 64$$

$$|m| < 8 \text{ (or } -8 < m < 8).$$

Therefore the values of m for which the graph of the parabola $y = x^2 + mx + 16$ is always above the x-axis are $-8 < m < 8$.

8.   *Solution*

The equation of a parabola with vertex $(4, 3)$ is of the form $y = a(x-4)^2 + 3$.

Since the point $(0, -29)$ is on the parabola, then

$$-29 = a(0-4)^2 + 3$$
$$16a = -32$$
$$a = -2.$$

Therefore the equation of the parabola is $y = -2(x-4)^2 + 3$.

When $x = 3$, $y = -2(3-4)^2 + 3 = 1$; and by symmetry, when $x = 5$, $y = 1$.

Therefore the rectangle has a base of 2 and a height of 1, and so its area is 2.

9.   *Solution*

For the x-intercepts, set $y = 0$:

$$x^2 - 8x + 7 = 0$$
$$(x-1)(x-7) = 0$$
$$x = 1 \text{ or } x = 7.$$

The points A and B are $(1, 0)$ and $(7, 0)$.

The vertex is at $x = \frac{1+7}{2} = 4$.

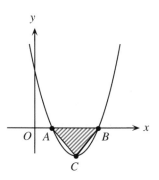

When $x = 4$, $y = 4^2 - 8(4) + 7 = -9$ and the vertex is $C(4, -9)$.

For $\triangle ABC$, the base has length $7 - 1 = 6$, and the height is 9.

Therefore the area of $\triangle ABC$ is $\frac{1}{2}(6 \times 9) = 27$.

10.   *Solution*

For $\sqrt{2-(1+x)^2}$ to be an integer, $2-(1+x)^2 \geq 0$.

Hence $0 \leq (1+x)^2 \leq 2$.

Therefore $(1+x)^2$ can be 0, 1, or 2.

If $(1+x)^2 = 0$, the given expression equals $\sqrt{2}$, which is not an integer.

If $(1+x)^2 = 2$, then $1+x = \pm\sqrt{2}$ and x is not an integer.

Hence $(1+x)^2 = 1$, which gives $x = -2$ or $x = 0$.

11. *Solution 1*

Let the point where they meet be C.

Then $\angle ACB = 45°, [180° - 90° - 45°]$

and so $\triangle ABC$ is isosceles.

Therefore $AC = 25$ km.

Then $BC = \sqrt{25^2 + 25^2} = 25\sqrt{2}$ km.

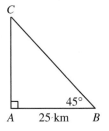

The runner covers 25 km in $\dfrac{25 \text{ km}}{10 \text{ km/h}} = 2.5$ hours.

The cyclist cycles for $2.5 - 0.5 = 2$ hours.

Therefore the speed of the cyclist is $\dfrac{25\sqrt{2}}{2} \cong 17.7$ km/h.

Solution 2

Let the cyclist's speed be k km/h.

Let the cyclist and the runner meet at C after t hours.

Therefore $AC = 10t$ km

and $BC = k\left(t - \dfrac{1}{2}\right)$ km.

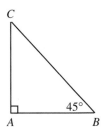

Since $\triangle ABC$ is isosceles (as in solution 1),

$\qquad AB = AC = 25$ km.

Therefore $10t = 25$ and so $t = 2.5$ hours.

Now, $BC = \sqrt{2}AB = 25\sqrt{2}$

$$k\left(t - \frac{1}{2}\right) = 25\sqrt{2}$$

$$k\left(2\frac{1}{2} - \frac{1}{2}\right) = 25\sqrt{2}$$

$$2k = 25\sqrt{2}$$

$$k = \frac{25\sqrt{2}}{2} \cong 17.7 \text{ km/h.}$$

Therefore the speed of the cyclist is 17.7 km/h.

12. *Solution*

$$p + pr + pr^2 = 26 \qquad\qquad (1)$$

$$p^2r + p^2r^2 + p^2r^3 = 156 \qquad (2)$$

From (1): $\qquad p\left(1 + r + r^2\right) = 26 \qquad (3)$

From (2): $\qquad p^2r\left(1 + r + r^2\right) = 156 \qquad (4)$

(4) ÷ (3) gives $\dfrac{p^2r}{p} = \dfrac{156}{26}$ or $pr = 6$.

Hence, $p = \frac{6}{r}$, and substituting in (3) we get

$$\frac{6}{r}\left(1 + r + r^2\right) = 26$$

$$6 + 6r + 6r^2 = 26r$$

$$6r^2 - 20r + 6 = 0$$

$$3r^2 - 10r + 3 = 0$$

$$(3r - 1)(r - 3) = 0$$

$$r = \frac{1}{3} \quad \text{or} \quad r = 3.$$

If $r = \frac{1}{3}$, then $p = 18$ and if $r = 3$, then $p = 2$.

13.   *Solution*
The distance travelled by the clown in one complete
circuit of the platform is 16 m, which takes

$$\frac{16\,\text{m}}{1.6\,\text{m}/\text{s}} = 10 \text{ seconds.}$$

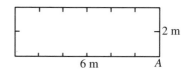

2 m

6 m   A

The distance, in metres, of the clown from his starting point and from point A at each of
$t = 0, 1, 2, ..., 10$ seconds is given in the table below.

t	0	1	2	3	4	5	6	7	8	9	10
distance from starting point	0	1.6	3.2	4.8	6.4	8.0	9.6	11.2	12.8	14.4	16
distance from A	−1	0.6	2.2	3.8	5.4	7.0	8.6	10.2	11.8	13.4	15

Since the platform has sides of length 6 m, the clown is walking along the sides when his
distance from A is between 0 and 6 metres and between 8 and 14 metres, i.e., at $t = 1, 2$,
3, 4, 6, 7, 8, 9 seconds during his first complete circuit.
Since the clown returns after 10 seconds to his starting point, he throws 8 candies per
complete circuit of the platform.
The platform travels for 6 km, at a rate of 1 m/s which will take 6000 seconds.

Therefore the clown throws $\frac{6000}{10} \times 8 = 4800$ candies to the crowd.

14. *Solution*

$$\left(x^2 - 3x + 1\right)^2 - 3\left(x^2 - 3x + 1\right) + 1 = x$$
$$x^4 + 9x^2 + 1 - 6x^3 + 2x^2 - 6x - 3x^2 + 9x - 3 + 1 = x$$
$$x^4 - 6x^3 + 8x^2 + 2x - 1 = 0.$$

Factoring, $\left(x^2 - 2x - 1\right)\left(x^2 - 4x + 1\right) = 0$

$$x^2 - 2x - 1 = 0 \quad \text{or} \quad x^2 - 4x + 1 = 0$$

$$x = \frac{2 \pm \sqrt{4 + 4}}{2} \qquad\qquad x = \frac{4 \pm \sqrt{16 - 4}}{2}$$

$$= 1 \pm \sqrt{2}. \qquad\qquad\qquad = 2 \pm \sqrt{3}.$$

Therefore $x = 1 \pm \sqrt{2}$ or $x = 2 \pm \sqrt{3}$.

15. *Solution 1*

The equation of the parabola can be written as

$$y = x^2 + 2x + 2k - 3$$
$$= x^2 + 2x + 1 - 1 + 2k - 3$$
$$= (x + 1)^2 + 2k - 4.$$

The vertex has coordinates $(-1, 2k - 4)$, and it will be on the x-axis when $2k - 4 = 0$ or $k = 2$.

Solution 2

To find the intersection of the x-axis and the parabola, we solve the equation $x^2 + 2x + 2k - 3 = 0$.
If the parabola has its vertex on the x-axis, then this equation has two real equal roots and so the discriminant $b^2 - 4ac$ equals 0.
Therefore $4 - 4(2k - 3) = 0$, giving $k = 2$.

There are two approaches to this problem. Solution 1 uses the fact that the difference in the times is 15 minutes. Solution 2 uses the fact that the distance is always the same.

16.   *Solution 1*
      Let d km be the distance between City A and City B.
      The following table presents distances (D), speeds (S) and times (T).

	D (km)	S (km/h)	T (h)
at 56 km/h	d	56	$\dfrac{d}{56}$
at 54 km/h	d	54	$\dfrac{d}{54}$

Then $\dfrac{d}{54} - \dfrac{d}{56} = \dfrac{1}{4}$

$$\dfrac{2d}{54(56)} = \dfrac{1}{4}$$

$$8d = 54(56)$$
$$d = 378.$$

Therefore the distance between City A and City B is 378 km.

Solution 2
Let t km be the scheduled time for the trip from City A to City B.
The following table presents distances (D), speeds (S) and times (T).

	D (km)	S (km/h)	T (h)
at 56 km/h	$56\left(t + \dfrac{27}{60}\right)$	56	$t + \dfrac{27}{60}$
at 54 km/h	$54\left(t + \dfrac{42}{60}\right)$	54	$t + \dfrac{42}{60}$

The equality becomes $56\left(t + \dfrac{27}{60}\right) = 54\left(t + \dfrac{42}{60}\right)$.

$$56t - 54t = \dfrac{54(42) - 56(27)}{60}$$
$$t = 6.3$$

The distance is equal to $56\left(6.3 + \dfrac{27}{60}\right) = 378$.

Therefore the distance between City A and City B is 378 km.

17. *Solution 1*

In one hour, nine large hoses fill $\frac{1}{4}$ of the pool, so one large hose fills $\frac{1}{9} \times \frac{1}{4} = \frac{1}{36}$ of the pool.

In one hour, six small hoses fill $\frac{1}{8}$ of the pool, so one small hose fills $\frac{1}{6} \times \frac{1}{8} = \frac{1}{48}$ of the pool.

In one hour, four large hoses and eight small hoses fill $4\left(\frac{1}{36}\right) + 8\left(\frac{1}{48}\right) = \frac{1}{9} + \frac{1}{6} = \frac{5}{18}$ of the pool.

Therefore it takes $3\frac{3}{5}$ hours to fill the pool.

Solution 2
9 large hoses fill the pool in 4 hours.

1 large hose fills $\frac{1}{9}$ of the pool in 4 hours.

4 large hoses fill $\frac{1}{9}$ of the pool in 1 hour.

6 small hoses fill the pool in 8 hours.

1 small hose fills $\frac{1}{6}$ of the pool in 8 hours.

8 small hoses fill $\frac{1}{6}$ of the pool in 1 hour.

Together, four large hoses and eight small hoses fill $\frac{1}{9} + \frac{1}{6} = \frac{5}{18}$ of the pool in 1 hour.

Therefore it will take $\frac{18}{5}$ hours to fill the pool.

18. *Solution*

If there are provisions for 5700 men for 66 days, there are 5700×66 daily food allowances [Note that we don't multiply this out. We will almost certainly have to tear it apart later!]

Since there are 5700 men initially, with a loss of 20 each day, we have an arithmetic sequence with $a = 5700$, $d = -20$, and we consider n days (n terms). The number of daily food allowances for n days is $S(n) = 5700 + 5680 + 5660 + ... + [5700 - 20(n-1)]$

$$= \frac{5700 + 5700 - 20(n-1)}{2} n$$
$$= 5710n - 10n^2.$$

Hence $5710n - 10n^2 = 5700 \times 66$

or $n^2 - 571n + (570 \times 66) = 0$.

[Now you can see why it was smart not to multiply those numbers together. We have to factor the product.]

Since $570 \times 66 = 2.3.5.19 \times 2.3.11$, we can determine that $571 = 495 + 76$ (from 3.3.5.11 $+ 2.2.19$) and $(n - 76)(n - 495) = 0$ so $n = 76$ or $n = 495$.

Are both answers correct?

If $n = 76$, by day 76 the number of food allowances consumed is, from $S(n)$, $5710 \times 76 - 10 \times 76^2$, or $376\,200$, which is 5700×66, and the number of men left is 4200.

If $n = 495$, then by day 495 the number of food allowances consumed is, from $S(n)$, $5710 \times 495 - 10 \times 495^2$, or $376\,200$, and the number of men left is -4180. This is clearly impossible.

We conclude that the supplies will hold out for 76 days.

19. *Solution*

    Case 1:   One side of the pasture does not extend past the end of the barn.

    Let x metres be the length of the barn wall that is not part of the pasture, $0 \le x \le 40$, and let y metres be the width of the pasture.

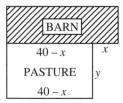

    Then the length of the pasture is $(40 - x)$ m.

    Hence, $(40 - x) + 2y = 100$

    $$y = \frac{60 + x}{2}.$$

The area is

$$A = (40 - x)\left(\frac{60 + x}{2}\right), \ 0 \le x \le 40$$

$$= -\frac{x^2}{2} - 10x + 1200$$

$$= -\frac{1}{2}(x + 10)^2 + 1250.$$

The function has a maximum value (of 1250) when $x = -10$.

But $x \ge 0$ and so the area has a maximum value when $x = 0$ and the maximum area is $40 \text{ m} \times 30 \text{ m} = 1200 \text{ m}^2$.

Case 2:   One side of the pasture extends past the end of the barn

Let x metres be the length of the pasture that extends past the barn, $x \ge 0$, and let y metres be the width of the pasture.

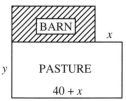

Then the length of the pasture is $(40 + x)$ m.

Hence, $(40 + x) + 2y + x = 100$

$$y = 30 - x.$$

The area is

$$A = (40 + x)(30 - x), \; 0 \le x \le 30$$
$$= -x^2 - 10x + 1200$$
$$= -(x+5)^2 + 1225.$$

The function has a maximum value (of 1225) when $x = -5$.

But $x \ge 0$ and so the area has a maximum value when $x = 0$ and the maximum area
is $40 \text{ m} \times 30 \text{ m} = 1200 \text{ m}^2$.

Therefore the maximum area is 1200 m^2.

20. *Solution*

Since p is a prime number that is a root of the equation, then $ap^4 + bp^3 + cp^2$ is an integer,
and $ap^4 + bp^3 + cp^2 - 630 = 0$.

Furthermore, since $630 = 3^2.2.5.7$, then $p^2\left(ap^2 + bp + c\right) = 3^2.2.5.7$.

Since the prime factor p appears twice on the left side and 3 is the only prime factor appearing
twice on the right side, $p = 3$.

Chapter 5
Answers to Exercises

1. $1104.71

2. $1000\left(e^{0.1}\right)^6 = \$1000e^{0.6} = \$1822.12$

    The difference is $\$1822.12 - \$1771.56 = \$50.56$.

4. If $x > 1$, $e^x > 1$; if $x < 0$, $0 < e^x < 1$.

5. Leonhard. He was a Swiss mathematician who lived between 1707 and 1783. He had 13 children and also produced a prodigeous amount of mathematics.

Solutions to Problems

1. *Solution*

    (a) $5^{2x-1} = 5^{2x} \cdot 5^{-1} = \dfrac{\left(5^x\right)^2}{5} = \dfrac{15^2}{5} = 45.$

    (b) $\log_3\left(\dfrac{\sqrt{3}}{2}\right) - \log_3\left(\dfrac{1}{2}\right) = \left(\log_3 \sqrt{3} - \log_3 2\right) - \left(\log_3 1 - \log_3 2\right)$

    $$= \frac{1}{3}\log_3 3 - \log_3 2 - 0 + \log_3 2$$

    $$= \frac{1}{3}.$$

    (c) $\log_8 18 = \log_8\left(2 \times 3^2\right) = \log_8 2 + 2\log_8 3$

    $$= \log_8 8^{\frac{1}{3}} + 2x$$

    $$= \frac{1}{3} + 2x.$$

2. *Solution*

    (a) $7^{x+2} - 7^x = 48\sqrt{7}$

    $$7^x\left(7^2 - 1\right) = 48\sqrt{7}$$

    $$7^x(48) = 48\left(7^{\frac{1}{2}}\right)$$

    $$7^x = 7^{\frac{1}{2}}$$

    $$x = \frac{1}{2}.$$

(b) $3^{2x} + 3^x = 20$

$3^{2x} + 3^x - 20 = 0.$

This is a quadratic equation in 3^x which we can factor.

$\left(3^x + 5\right)\left(3^x - 4\right) = 0$

But $3^x > 0$ so $3^x \neq -5.$

Hence $3^x = 4$

$x \log 3 = \log 4$

$x = \dfrac{\log 4}{\log 3}.$

(c)   Multiply the numerator and denominator of $\dfrac{1}{2^{1990}}$ by 2.

Hence $\dfrac{2}{2^{1991}} - \dfrac{1}{2^{1991}} = 2^x$

$\dfrac{1}{2^{1991}} = 2^x$

$x = -1991.$

3.   *Solution*

$9x^2 - 28x + 3 = 0$

$(9x - 1)(x - 3) = 0$

$x = \dfrac{1}{9} \quad or \quad x = 3.$

Hence $\log_3 r + \log_3 s = \log_3 rs$

$= \log_3 \left(\dfrac{1}{9}\right)(3)$

$= \log_3 \left(3^{-1}\right)$

$= -1.$

Note that the product of the roots is $rs = \dfrac{3}{9} = 3^{-1}.$

Therefore $\log_3 r + \log_3 s = \log_3 rs = -1.$

4.   *Solution*

Since the point $(4, 1)$ is on the graph of $y = \log_a x$, then $1 = \log_a 4$ and so $a = 4.$

[If the point $(16, 2)$ is used, then $2 = \log_a 16$, so $a^2 = 16$ and $a = 4$, since $a > 0$; if the point $(0.25, -1)$ is used, then $0.25 = \dfrac{1}{4} = 4^{-1}$, $-1 = \log_a \left(\dfrac{1}{4}\right)$, so $a^{-1} = \dfrac{1}{4}$ and hence $a = 4.$]

5. *Solution*

$$\log_x \frac{9}{2} x^2 = \log_x 9 + \log_x x^2 - \log_x 2$$

$$= 2\log_x 3 + 2\log_x x - \log_x 2$$

$$= 2b + 2 - a.$$

6. *Solution*

Rewrite the equations as

$$3^{2x-y} = 3^3$$

$$2^{3x+2y} = 2^5$$

Equating exponents gives us

$$2x - y = 3$$

$$3x + 2y = 5$$

Solving this system we get $x = \frac{11}{7}$, $y = \frac{1}{7}$.

7. *Solution*

Since logarithms are defined only for positive numbers a solution is possible only if $x > 3$.

Now $\log_2(3x+4) - \log_2(x-3) = 3$

$$\log_2 \frac{3x+4}{x-3} = 3.$$

Changing to exponential form we get

$$\frac{3x+4}{x-3} = 2^3$$

$$3x + 4 = 8x - 24.$$

The solution is $x = \frac{28}{5}$.

8. *Solution*

$$\log_{10}\left(\frac{3}{2}\right) + \log_{10}\left(\frac{4}{3}\right) + \log_{10}\left(\frac{5}{4}\right) + \cdots + \log_{10}\left(\frac{200}{199}\right)$$

$$= \log_{10}\left(\frac{3}{2} \times \frac{4}{3} \times \frac{5}{4} \times \cdots \times \frac{200}{199}\right)$$

$$= \log_{10}\left(\frac{200}{2}\right)$$

$$= \log_{10} 100$$

$$= 2.$$

As an alternate approach, use $\log_{10}\frac{a}{b} = \log_{10} a - \log_{10} b$ for each term in the series.

9.   *Solution*

$$g[f(100)] = g(49^{300})$$

$$= \log_7(49^{300})$$

$$= 300 \log_7 49$$

$$= 300(2)$$

$$= 600.$$

10.   *Solution*

Since $\log x^2 = a$, $\log y^3 = b$ and $\log xy = c$

then $2 \log x = a$ (1)

$3 \log y = b$ (2)

and $\log x + \log y = c$ (3)

Multiply equation (1) by 3, equation (2) by 2 and add to give

$$6 \log x + 6 \log y = 3a + 2b$$

$$6(\log x + \log y) = 3a + 2b$$

Therefore $6c = 3a + 2b$.

11.   *Solution*

Since $\log_2(9 - 2^x) = 3 - x$, therefore $9 - 2^x = 2^{3-x}$.

Multiply by 2^x:

$$9.2^x - 2^{2x} = 2^3$$

$$2^{2x} - 9.2^x + 8 = 0.$$

Factoring as a quadratic in 2^x we get

$$(2^x - 1)(2^x - 8) = 0$$

$$2^x = 1 \text{ or } 2^x = 8$$

$$x = 0 \text{ or } x = 3.$$

12.   *Solution*

Proof: If we multiply the numerator and denominator of $\dfrac{e^{-x}}{e^{-x} + 1}$ by e^x we get $\dfrac{1}{1 + e^x}$.

Hence $\dfrac{e^{-x}}{e^{-x} + 1} + \dfrac{e^x}{e^x + 1} = \dfrac{1}{1 + e^x} + \dfrac{e^x}{e^x + 1}$

$$= 1.$$

13. *Solution*

Proof: Let $\dfrac{x}{n} = \dfrac{1}{m}$.

Then $mx = n$ and we note that as $n \to \infty$, $m \to \infty$.

Thus $\displaystyle\lim_{n\to\infty}\left(1+\dfrac{x}{n}\right)^n = \lim_{m\to\infty}\left(1+\dfrac{1}{m}\right)^{mx}$

$$= \lim_{m\to\infty}\left[\left(1+\dfrac{1}{m}\right)^m\right]^x$$

$$= e^x.$$

In this proof we have used a property of limits that is beyond the scope of this book.

14. *Solution*

Taking logarithms, base 10, of both sides of the inequality gives us

$$n \log \frac{21}{20} < \log 100$$

$$n(\log 21 - \log 20) < 2$$

$$n < \frac{2}{\log 21 - \log 20}.$$

The right side has a value of approximately 94.387.

The largest integer value for n will be 94.

15. *Solution*

Since $\log_x a = m$ and $\log_y a = n$, then $x^m = a$ and $y^n = a$.

Therefore $x^{mn} = a^n$ and $y^{mn} = a^m$.

Dividing these equations we get

$$\left(\frac{x}{y}\right)^{mn} = a^{n-m}$$

$$\log_{\frac{x}{y}}\left(\frac{x}{y}\right)^{mn} = \log_{\frac{x}{y}} a^{n-m}$$

$$mn = (n-m)\log_{\frac{x}{y}} a.$$

Hence $\log_{\frac{x}{y}} a = \dfrac{mn}{n-m}$.

16. *Solution*

Proof: We will use the result from the earlier discussions that $\log_a b = \dfrac{1}{\log_b a}$. In

particular $\log_e b = \ln b = \dfrac{1}{\log_b e}$.

Therefore $S = \ln 2 + \ln 3 + \ln 4 + \dots + \ln 20$

$$= \ln(2 \cdot 3 \cdot 4 \cdot \dots \cdot 20)$$

$$= \ln(20!).$$

17. *Solution 1*

In order to have the minimum number of prizes, we must have as many of the larger prizes as possible.

Convert $1\,000\,000$ to base 11:

$$1\,000\,000 = 11(90\,909) + 1$$
$$90\,909 = 11(8264) + 5$$
$$8264 = 11(751) + 3$$
$$751 = 11(68) + 3$$
$$68 = 11(6) + 2$$
$$6 = 11(0) + 6$$

Therefore $1\,000\,000_{10} = 623\,351_{11}$

$$= 6(11^5) + 2(11^4) + 3(11^3) + 3(11^2) + 5(11^1) + 1(11^0).$$

Therefore the minimum number of prizes is $6 + 2 + 3 + 3 + 5 + 1 = 20$.

Solution 2

If we award 6 prizes of $\$11^5$, we have used $\$966\,306$, leaving $\$33\,694$.

If we award 2 prizes of $\$11^4$, we have used $\$29\,282$, leaving $\$4412$.

If we award 3 prizes of $\$11^3$, we have used $\$3993$, leaving $\$419$.

If we award 3 prizes of $\$11^2$, we have used $\$363$, leaving $\$56$.

If we award 5 prizes of $\$11$, we have used $\$55$, leaving $\$1$.

If we award 1 prize of $\$11^0 = \$1$, we have used $\$1$, leaving $\$0$.

Therefore the minimum number of prizes is $6 + 2 + 3 + 3 + 5 + 1 = 20$.

18. *Solution*

Since the logarithm function is an increasing one, the statement

$1995^{1994} < 1994^n < 1995^{1995}$ is satisfied if and only if

$\log 1995^{1994} < \log 1994^n < \log 1995^{1995}$, that is,

$$1994 \log 1995 < n \log 1994 < 1995 \log 1995$$

$$1994 \frac{\log 1995}{\log 1994} < n < 1995 \frac{\log 1995}{\log 1994} \quad \text{(since } \log 1994 > 0).$$

If n lies between these two numbers, and the difference between them exceeds one, then there is an integer in the interval

$$1995 \frac{\log 1995}{\log 1994} - 1994 \frac{\log 1995}{\log 1994} = \frac{\log 1995}{\log 1994}.$$

The logarithm function is an increasing one, so $\log 1995 > \log 1994$. Hence

$$\frac{\log 1995}{\log 1994} > 1.$$

Hence the interval between these numbers is greater than 1 and there is an integer n satisfying the relation.

19. *Solution*

We will use a proof by contradiction.

Proof: Assume that e is a rational number. If this is true we can write $e = \frac{a}{b}$, where a and b are integers and the fraction $\frac{a}{b}$ is in its reduced form. That is, the greatest common divisor of a and b is 1.

$$e = \frac{a}{b} = 1 + \frac{1}{1!} + \frac{1}{2!} + \frac{1}{3!} + \cdots + \frac{1}{(b-1)!} + \frac{1}{b!} + \frac{1}{(b+1)!} + \frac{1}{(b+2)} + \cdots.$$

Multiply by $b!$:

$$\frac{ab!}{b} = b! + \frac{b!}{1!} + \frac{b!}{2!} + \frac{b!}{3!} + \cdots + \frac{b!}{(b-1)!} + \frac{b!}{b!} + \frac{b!}{(b+1)!} + \frac{b!}{(b+2)!} + \cdots$$

$$a(b-1)! = \left(b! + \frac{b!}{1!} + \frac{b!}{2!} + \frac{b!}{3!} + \cdots + b + 1 \right) + \left(\frac{1}{(b+1)} + \frac{1}{(b+1)(b+2)} + \cdots \right).$$

Now $a(b-1)!$ is an integer and the first bracket on the right side is also an integer. So the equation is of the form $I_1 = I_2 + \left(\frac{1}{b+1} + \frac{1}{(b+1)(b+2)} + \frac{1}{(b+1)(b+2)(b+3)} + \cdots \right).$

Can we prove that this last bracket is not an integer?

$$Q = \frac{1}{b+1} + \frac{1}{(b+1)(b+2)} + \frac{1}{(b+1)(b+2)(b+3)} + \cdots$$

$$< \frac{1}{b+1} + \frac{1}{(b+1)(b+1)} + \frac{1}{(b+1)(b+1)(b+1)} + \cdots$$

$$= \frac{1}{b+1} + \frac{1}{(b+1)^2} + \frac{1}{(b+1)^3} + \cdots$$

This is an infinite geometric series of positive numbers with first term $\frac{1}{b+1}$ and common ratio $\frac{1}{b+1}$.

Its sum is $\dfrac{\frac{1}{b+1}}{1 - \frac{1}{b+1}} = \dfrac{1}{(b+1)-1} = \dfrac{1}{b} \leq 1.$

Hence $0 < Q < 1$ and we have $I_1 = I_2 + Q$ which is impossible. Our assumption that e is rational is false so we conclude that e is irrational.

Note: Based on writing $e = 1 + \frac{1}{1!} + \frac{1}{2!} + \frac{1}{3!} + \cdots$ you might predict (correctly) that

$$e^x = 1 + \frac{x}{1!} + \frac{x^2}{2!} + \frac{x^3}{3!} + \cdots.$$

Find an approximate value of e^2 by evaluating the first five terms of this series.

Chapter 6
Answers to Exercises

1. Richard Feynman (1918 - 1988) was an American physicist who was involved in the development of the atomic bomb. In 1965 he won the Nobel Prize for Physics.

    You can find out more about this eccentric character by reading "Genius" by James Gleick, Abacus, London, 1992, "Surely You're Joking, Mr. Feynman!" by R.K. Feynman, Unwin paperback, 1986 or "What Do **You** Care What Other People Think?" by R.K. Feynman, Unwin Hyman, 1988.

2. Using the difference in air pressure between the top and the bottom of the building.

3. There are more methods to come. Read on.

4. (a) (i) $\dfrac{1}{\sqrt{2}}$ (ii) $\dfrac{1}{\sqrt{2}}$ (iii) $-\dfrac{1}{\sqrt{2}}$ (iv) $-\dfrac{1}{\sqrt{2}}$ (v) $-\dfrac{1}{\sqrt{2}}$ (vi) 1

    (viii) -1

    (b) (i) $\dfrac{\sqrt{3}}{2}$ (ii) $\dfrac{1}{2}$ (iii) $\dfrac{\sqrt{3}}{2}$ (iv) $-\dfrac{\sqrt{3}}{2}$ (v) $-\dfrac{\sqrt{3}}{2}$ (vi) 0

    (vii) $-\sqrt{3}$ (viii) $-\dfrac{1}{\sqrt{3}}$ (ix) $-\sqrt{3}$

5. If you measure θ_1, θ_2 and a, I think you can calculate h.

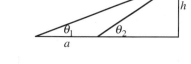

6. 360° at the centre of the circle is subtended by the whole of the circumference. This length is $2\pi r$, so 360° is equivalent to 2π radians.

7. 180 degrees = π radians; 45 degrees = $\dfrac{\pi}{4}$ radians.

8. $\dfrac{1}{3}\pi = 60$ degrees; $\dfrac{7\pi}{6} = 210$ degrees.

9. (a) Draw a good diagram showing an angle of size θ and one of size $-\theta$ and use congruent triangles.

    (b) A similar argument to (a) gives $\cos(-\theta) = \cos\theta$.

    (c) Use a similar argument to (a) to show that $\tan(-\theta) = -\tan\theta$.

10. (a) This can be argued very nicely by using the same diagram as in exercise 9.

    (b) Use a similar argument to part (a) to show that $|\cos \theta| \leq 1$.

    (c) No. Again, a diagram allows you to see this.

11. To sketch $y = \cos \theta$, note that $\cos \theta = \sin \left(\frac{\pi}{2} - \theta\right)$. Both of these graphs are drawn in section 2.

18. (i)   (ii)

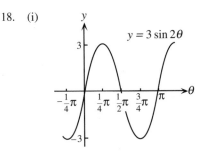

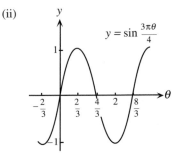

(iii)   (iv)

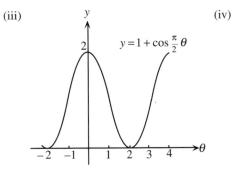

(v) The same graph as $y = \tan \theta$.   (vi)

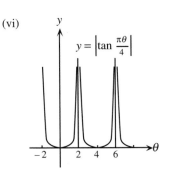

Solutions to Problems

1.   *Solution*

$$2\sin^2 x - 3\sin x - 2 = 0$$

$$(2\sin x + 1)(\sin x - 2) = 0$$

$$\sin x = -\frac{1}{2} \quad \text{or} \quad \sin x = 2.$$

Since $-1 \le \sin x \le 1$, we discard $\sin x = 2$.

If $\sin x = -\frac{1}{2}$, $x = -\frac{\pi}{6}$ or $-\frac{5\pi}{6}$.

2.   *Solution*

From $6\cos^2 \theta - \sin \theta = 4$ we obtain

$$6\left(1 - \sin^2 \theta\right) - \sin \theta = 4$$

$$6\sin^2 \theta + \sin \theta - 2 = 0$$

$$(3\sin \theta + 2)(2\sin \theta - 1) = 0$$

$$\sin \theta = -\frac{2}{3} \quad \text{or} \quad \sin \theta = \frac{1}{2}.$$

For $0 \le \theta \le \pi$, $\sin \theta \ge 0$. Hence there is no value of θ for which $\sin \theta = -\frac{2}{3}$. For

$\sin \theta = \frac{1}{2}$, $\theta = \frac{\pi}{6}$ or $\frac{5\pi}{6}$.

3.   *Solution*

$$\cos(2\theta) = -\frac{7}{9}$$

$$2\cos^2 \theta - 1 = -\frac{7}{9}$$

$$\cos^2 \theta = \frac{1}{9}.$$

Thus $\cos \theta = \frac{1}{3}$ since $0 < \theta < \frac{\pi}{2}$.

4.   *Solution*

$$\text{LHS} = \frac{\sin \theta}{\cos \theta} + \frac{\cos \theta}{\sin \theta}$$

$$= \frac{\sin^2 \theta + \cos^2 \theta}{\sin \theta \cos \theta}$$

$$= \frac{1}{\frac{1}{2}\sin(2\theta)}$$

$$= \frac{2}{\sin(2\theta)}.$$

The identity is true.

5.   *Solution*

$$\text{LHS} = 1 - \frac{\sin^2 \theta}{1 + \frac{\cos \theta}{\sin \theta}} - \frac{\cos^2 \theta}{1 + \frac{\sin \theta}{\cos \theta}}$$

$$= 1 - \frac{\sin^2 \theta}{\frac{\sin \theta + \cos \theta}{\sin \theta}} - \frac{\cos^2 \theta}{\frac{\cos \theta + \sin \theta}{\cos \theta}}$$

$$= 1 - \frac{\sin^3 \theta + \cos^3 \theta}{\sin \theta + \cos \theta}$$

$$= 1 - \frac{(\sin \theta + \cos \theta)(\sin^2 \theta - \sin \theta \cos \theta + \cos^2 \theta)}{\sin \theta \cos \theta}$$

$$= 1 - (1 - \sin \theta \cos \theta)$$

$$= \sin \theta \cos \theta$$

$$= \frac{1}{2} \sin (2\theta).$$

Hence the identity is true.

6.   *Solution*

$$\text{LHS} = 1 + \tan (2x) \tan x$$

$$= 1 + \frac{\sin (2x) \sin x}{\cos (2x) \cos x}$$

$$= 1 + \frac{2 \sin^2 x \cos x}{\cos(2x) \cos x}$$

$$= \frac{\cos (2x) + 2 \sin^2 x}{\cos (2x)}$$

$$= \frac{\cos^2 x - \sin^2 x + 2 \sin^2 x}{\cos (2x)}$$

$$= \frac{1}{\cos (2x)}$$

$$= \text{RHS.}$$

Hence the identity is true.

7. *Solution*

$$\text{LHS} = \frac{2 \sin (2x)\cos (2x)}{1 - \left(1 - 2 \sin^2(2x)\right)}$$

$$= \frac{2 \sin (2x) \cos (2x)}{2 \sin^2(2x)}$$

$$= \frac{\cos (2x)}{\sin (2x)}.$$

$$\text{RHS} = \frac{\cos x}{\sin x} - \frac{1}{2 \sin x \cos x}$$

$$= \frac{2 \cos^2 x - 1}{2 \sin x \cos x}$$

$$= \frac{\cos (2x)}{\sin (2x)}.$$

Hence $\dfrac{\sin (4x)}{1 - \cos (4x)} = \cot x - \dfrac{1}{2}\csc x \sec x.$

8. (a) *Solution*

$$\log_{10}(\tan A) + \log_{10}(\cos A)$$

$$= \log_{10}(\tan A \cdot \cos A)$$

$$= \log_{10}\left(\frac{\sin A}{\cos A} \cdot \cos A\right)$$

$$= \log_{10}(\sin A)$$

$$= \log_{10}(0.1)$$

$$= -1.$$

(b) *Solution*
If $\sin 2t = 0$,
$2t = 0, \ \pm \pi, \ \pm 2\pi, \ \pm 3\pi, \dots$

$t = 0, \ \pm \dfrac{\pi}{2}, \ \pm \pi, \ \pm \dfrac{3\pi}{2}, \dots$

Therefore $\sin 2t = 0$, 1 or -1.
Hence there are three possible values for $\sin t$.

(c)   *Solution*

$$\sin^2 \theta = 1 - \cos \theta$$
$$1 - \cos^2 \theta = 1 - \cos \theta$$
$$\cos^2 \theta - \cos \theta = 0$$
$$\cos \theta (\cos \theta - 1) = 0$$

$\cos \theta = 0$ or $\cos \theta = 1$.

If $\cos \theta = 0$, $0 \le \theta \le 2\pi$, then $\theta = \dfrac{\pi}{2}$ or $\theta = \dfrac{3\pi}{2}$.

If $\cos \theta = 1$, $0 \le \theta \le 2\pi$, then $\theta = 0$ or $\theta = 2\pi$.

Therefore the roots are 0, $\dfrac{\pi}{2}, \dfrac{3\pi}{2}$, and 2π.

9.   *Solution*
The smallest positive value of θ for which $\cos \theta = \sin \theta$ is $\theta = 45°$.
Hence, $9x = 45$
$$x = 5.$$

10.   *Solution*

If $2 \sin (2\theta) + 1 = 0$, then $\sin (2\theta) = -\dfrac{1}{2}$.

From the diagram, the smallest positive value of θ
will be in the second quadrant.

Since $\sin 210° = -\dfrac{1}{2}$,
$$2\theta = 210°$$
$$\theta = 105°.$$

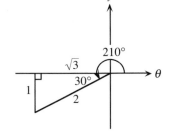

11.   *Solution*
If r is the radius of the circle, then

$$\frac{\text{arc } AB}{\text{circumference}} = \frac{150}{360}$$
$$\frac{5\pi}{2\pi r} = \frac{150}{360} = \frac{5}{12}$$
$$2r = 12$$
$$r = 6.$$

By the Cosine Law, $(AB)^2 = 6^2 + 6^2 - 2(6)(6)\cos 150°$

$$= 36 + 36 - 72\left(-\frac{\sqrt{3}}{2}\right)$$

$$= 72 + 36\sqrt{3}.$$

$$(AB)^2 \cong 72 + 36(1.732) = 134.352.$$

Therefore $AB = 11.6$, (correct to one decimal place).

12. *Solution*
     In triangle ABC,

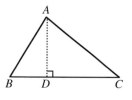

$$\sin B = \frac{AD}{AB} = \frac{3}{5}.$$

Let $AD = 3$ and $AB = 5$.

Also, $\sin C = \dfrac{AD}{AC} = \dfrac{1}{4} = \dfrac{3}{12}$.

Thus $AC = 12$.

Then $DC^2 = AC^2 - AD^2$

$$= 144 - 9$$

$$= 135.$$

$$DC = 3\sqrt{15}.$$

Also $BD^2 = AB^2 - AD^2$

$$= 16.$$

$$BD = 4.$$

The ratio $AB : BC$ is $5 : 4 + 3\sqrt{15}$.

13. *Solution*
     Consider the diagram.
     Since $m = AD - BD$, we require AD and BD in
     terms of h and the given angles.

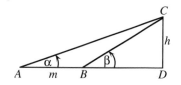

     In $\triangle ACD$, $\dfrac{AD}{h} = \cot \alpha$

$$AD = h \cot \alpha.$$

Similarly $BD = h \cot \beta$.

Then $m = h(\cot \alpha - \cot \beta)$

$$\text{and } h = \frac{m}{\cot \alpha - \cot \beta}.$$

14. *Solution*

The graph of $y = \cos(4\theta)$ has an amplitude of 1 and period $\frac{\pi}{2}$.

The graph of $y = \sin(3\theta)$ has an amplitude of 1 and period $\frac{2\pi}{3}$.

In the interval $0 \le \theta \le \frac{\pi}{2}$ the graphs intersect in two points.

Thus the equation $\cos(4\theta) = \sin(3\theta)$ has two solutions in this interval.

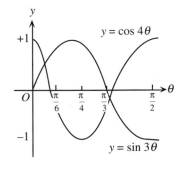

15. *Solution*

The given graph of the sine curve has an amplitude of 2 and a period of π, so its equation is $y = 2\sin(2x)$.

When $y = 1$, $2\sin(2x) = 1$

$$\sin(2x) = \frac{1}{2}.$$

Therefore, $2x = \frac{\pi}{6}, \frac{5\pi}{6}, \ldots$

$$x = \frac{\pi}{12}, \frac{5\pi}{12}, \ldots$$

The coordinates of D are $\left(\frac{\pi}{12}, 1\right)$.

16. *Solution*

(i)

(ii)

(iii) From the graph, $f(\theta) = 0$ for $\theta = 0$ or $\pi \le \theta \le 2\pi$.

17. *Solution*

$$(2 \sin x \cos x)^2 - \sin^2 x = 2 \sin^2 x \cos x$$

$$\sin^2 x \left(4\cos^2 x - 2 \cos x - 1\right) = 0$$

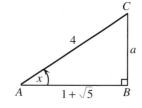

$$\sin x = 0 \quad \text{or} \quad \cos x = \frac{2 \pm \sqrt{4 + 16}}{8} = \frac{1 \pm \sqrt{5}}{4}.$$

Since $0 \le x \le \frac{\pi}{2}$, $\cos x = \frac{1 + \sqrt{5}}{4}.$

In $\triangle ABC$, $a^2 + \left(1 + \sqrt{5}\right)^2 = 4^2$

$$a^2 = 10 - 2\sqrt{5}$$

$$a = \sqrt{10 - 2\sqrt{5}}.$$

The possible values of $\sin x$ are 0 and $\dfrac{\sqrt{10 - 2\sqrt{5}}}{4}.$

18. *Solution*

For the equation to have real roots, $D \ge 0$, where $D = b^2 - 4ac$.

$$(2 \sin \theta)^2 - 4 \cos (2\theta) \ge 0$$

$$4 \sin^2 \theta - 4\left(1 - 2 \sin^2 \theta\right) \ge 0$$

$$\sin^2 \theta \ge \frac{1}{3}.$$

Then $\sin \theta \ge \dfrac{1}{\sqrt{3}}$ or $\sin \theta \le -\dfrac{1}{\sqrt{3}}.$

But we are given that $-\dfrac{\pi}{2} \le \theta \le \dfrac{\pi}{2}.$

We conclude that the roots are real if $\theta \ge \sin^{-1}\left(\dfrac{1}{\sqrt{3}}\right)$ and $\theta \le \dfrac{\pi}{2}$,

that is, if $\sin^{-1}\left(\dfrac{1}{\sqrt{3}}\right) \le \theta \le \dfrac{\pi}{2}$ or if $-\dfrac{\pi}{2} \le \theta \le \sin^{-1}\left(-\dfrac{1}{\sqrt{3}}\right).$

If a calculator is used, $\sin^{-1}\left(\dfrac{1}{\sqrt{3}}\right) \doteq .62$ radians.

19. *Solution*

$$x^2 - 4x + 6 = x^2 - 4x + 4 + 2$$
$$= (x-2)^2 + 2$$

and so $x^2 - 4x + 6$ has a minimum value of 2, which occurs only when $x = 2$. The expression $2 \sin x$ has a maximum value of 2, which occurs only when

$$x = \ldots, -\frac{3\pi}{2}, \frac{\pi}{2}, \frac{5\pi}{2}, \ldots .$$

Hence at $x = 2$, which is not in the above set, $2 \sin x < 2$.

Therefore there are no real values of x such that $2 \sin x = x^2 - 4x + 6$.

20. *Solution*

Label the corners of the box as shown.
Construct NQ perpendicular to the ground,
intersecting the horizontal line through A at P.
Join AN.

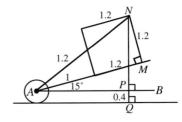

In $\triangle ANM$, $AN = \sqrt{(1.2)^2 + (2.2)^2} \cong 2.506$ m

and $\angle NAM = \tan^{-1} \dfrac{1.2}{2.2} \cong 28.61°$.

In $\triangle ANP$, $NP \cong 2.506 \sin(28.61 + 15)° \cong 1.7$ m

$$NQ = NP + PQ$$
and so $\qquad \cong 1.7 + 0.4$
$$= 2.1 \text{ m}.$$

Therefore the minimum height of the doorway is 2.1 m.

21. *Solution*

The period of both functions is $\dfrac{2\pi}{\frac{1}{2}}$ or 4π.

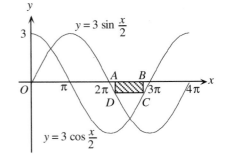

Let the point A have coordinates $(t, 0)$.

Then point B has coordinates $\left(t + \dfrac{\pi}{3}, 0\right)$.

If the figure is a rectangle $AD = BC$, and

$$\sin\left(\frac{t}{2}\right) = \cos\left(\frac{t}{2} + \frac{\pi}{6}\right)$$

$$= \cos\left(\frac{t}{2}\right)\cos\frac{\pi}{6} - \sin\frac{t}{2}\sin\frac{\pi}{6}$$

$$= \frac{\sqrt{3}}{2}\cos\left(\frac{t}{2}\right) - \frac{1}{2}\sin\frac{t}{2}.$$

Then $\dfrac{3}{2}\sin\left(\dfrac{t}{2}\right) = \dfrac{\sqrt{3}}{2}\cos\left(\dfrac{t}{2}\right)$ or $\tan\left(\dfrac{t}{2}\right) = \dfrac{1}{\sqrt{3}}$.

Hence $\dfrac{t}{2} = \dfrac{\pi}{6}, \dfrac{7\pi}{6}, \dfrac{13\pi}{6}, \dots$, and since $2\pi < t < 3\pi$, $\dfrac{t}{2} = \dfrac{7\pi}{6}$ and $t = \dfrac{7\pi}{3}$.

Then $AD = \left| 3\sin\dfrac{\pi}{6} \right| = \left| 3\left(-\dfrac{1}{2}\right) \right| = \dfrac{3}{2}$.

The area of the rectangle is $\dfrac{\pi}{3} \cdot \dfrac{3}{2}$ or $\dfrac{\pi}{2}$.

Chapter 7
Answers to Exercises

1.   We're getting closer and closer to 2.

2.   Did you get 6?

3.   2a. (How did you do this?)

4.   Doesn't this depend on where the point (a, b) is?

5.   See Problem 1 in Section 7.4.

6.   Is the answer two tangents for a point below the curve in the first quadrant and above the curve in the third quadrant, and one tangent everywhere else?

7.   With $P(3, 3)$ and $Q\left(3+h, (3+h)^2\right)$, the gradient of PQ is

$$\frac{(3+h)^2 - 3^2}{(3+h) - 3} = \frac{h^2 + 6h}{h} = h + 6.$$

8.   With $P(2, 4)$ and $Q\left(2+h, (2+h)^2 - 2(2+h)\right)$, the gradient of PQ is

$$\frac{(2+h)^3 - 2(2+h) - 4}{2+h-2} = \frac{h^3 + 6h^2 + 10h}{h} = h^2 + 6h + 10. \text{ As } h \to 0, \text{ this gradient}$$
approaches 10.

9.   Over to you.

10. $\dfrac{dy}{dx} = \lim\limits_{h \to 0} \left(\dfrac{f(a+h) - f(a)}{h} \right).$

Solutions to Problems

1.   *Solution*
      The slope of the tangent to the given curve at any point (x, y) is given by

$$\frac{dy}{dx} = \frac{1}{2}\left(x^2 + 3\right)^{-\frac{1}{2}}(2x) = \frac{x}{\sqrt{x^2 + 3}}.$$

When $x = 1$, $y = \sqrt{1+3} = 2$, so the contact point of the tangent is $(1, 2)$. At this point,

the slope of the tangent is $\dfrac{1}{\sqrt{1+3}} = \dfrac{1}{2}$.

The equation of the required tangent is $\dfrac{y-2}{x-1} = \dfrac{1}{2}$ or $x - 2y + 3 = 0.$

2. *Solution*

The slope of the tangent to the curve at point (x, y) is given by $\dfrac{dy}{dx} = 6x^2 - 8$.

When the slope is -2, we obtain $6x^2 - 8 = -2$

$$6x^2 = 6$$
$$x = \pm 1.$$

When $x = 1$, $y = 2(1)^3 - 8(1) + 40 = 34$.

When $x = -1$, $y = 2(-1)^3 - 8(-1) + 40 = 46$.

The two tangent contact points are $(1, 34)$ and $(-1, 46)$.

The equation of the tangent at $(1, 34)$ with slope -2 is

$$y - 34 = -2(x - 1)$$

or $\qquad y = -2x + 36$.

The equation of the tangent at $(-1, 46)$ with slope -2 is

$$y - 46 = -2(x + 1)$$

or $\qquad y = -2x + 44$.

3. *Solution*

The slope of the tangent at point (x, y) to $y^2 = 8x$ is given by

$$2y\dfrac{dy}{dx} = 8 \ \text{ or } \ \dfrac{dy}{dx} = \dfrac{4}{y}.$$

If this tangent is parallel to the line $y = 4x + 5$, then $\dfrac{4}{y} = 4$ and $y = 1$.

From $y^2 = 8x$, $x = \dfrac{1}{8}$ when $y = 1$, and the contact point is $\left(\dfrac{1}{8}, 1\right)$. The tangent slope is 4.

The equation of the tangent is

$$y - 1 = 4\left(x - \dfrac{1}{8}\right) \ \text{ or } \ 8x - 2y + 1 = 0.$$

4. *Solution*

The slope of the tangent at any point (x, y) is given by

$$y'(x) = 2(x - 1)(4 - x) - (x - 1)^2 = -3x^2 + 12x - 9.$$

The slope function has a maximum when its derivative is zero.

That is, $\quad y''(x) = -6x + 12 = 0$

$$x = 2.$$

The graph of $y = y'(x)$ is a parabola opening down since the coefficient of x^2 is negative, so $x = 2$ does give a maximum.

The maximum slope is $y'(2) = 3$.

The point of contact of the tangent and the curve is $(2, y)$ where $y = (2 - 1)^2(4 - 2) = 2$.

The tangent equation is $y - 2 = 3(x - 2)$ or $y = 3x - 4$.

5. *Solution*

Since the function is a polynomial, extrema occur at points whose x-coordinates are determined from $\dfrac{dy}{dx} = 0$.

Hence consider

$$4x^3 + 12x^2 - 16x = 0$$
$$x(x+4)(x-1) = 0$$
$$x = 0, -4, 1.$$

The extreme points (and hence the vertices of the triangle) are $A(0,0)$, $B(-4,-128)$ and $C(1,-3)$.

The area of triangle ABC is given by

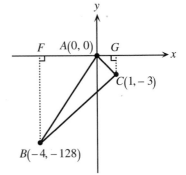

$$\text{trapezoid } FBCG - \Delta ABF - \Delta AGC$$
$$= \tfrac{1}{2}(128+3)5 - \tfrac{1}{2}(128)4 - \tfrac{1}{2}(3)1$$
$$= 70.$$

6. *Solution*

Let x m be the distance the person is from the wall at time t seconds, and let h m be the height of the shadow on the wall at this time.

Label the diagram as shown, so $PR = 6-x$, $LR = 3$, $PQ = 2-h$.

Since $SQ \parallel PR$ and $PQ \parallel LR$, ΔSQP and ΔPRL will be equiangular and hence similar.

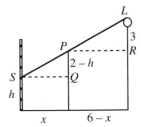

Therefore $\dfrac{x}{6-x} = \dfrac{2-h}{3}$

or $xh - 5x - 6h + 12 = 0$.

Differentiating with respect to t,

$$x\frac{dh}{dt} + h\frac{dx}{dt} - 5\frac{dx}{dt} - 6\frac{dh}{dt} = 0$$

$$(h-5)\frac{dx}{dt} + (x-6)\frac{dh}{dt} = 0.$$

Now $\dfrac{dx}{dt} = 1.2$, so $\dfrac{dh}{dt} = -\dfrac{1.2(h-5)}{x-6}$.

At the required time $x = 1.5$. Substituting this in the original function we obtain

$$1.5h - 7.5 - 6h + 12 = 0$$
$$h = 1.$$

Now putting $x = 1.5$, $h = 1$ in the expression for $\dfrac{dh}{dt}$,

$$\dfrac{dh}{dt} = -\dfrac{1.2(4)}{(-4.5)}$$

$$= -\dfrac{16}{15}.$$

The shadow is descending at $\dfrac{16}{15}$ metres per second.

7. *Solution*

Let the coordinates of P be $\left(a, \dfrac{8}{a}\right)$, with $a > 0$.

The slope of the tangent to the curve at any point (x, y) is given by $\dfrac{dy}{dx} = -\dfrac{8}{x^2}$, so the slope at P is $-\dfrac{8}{a^2}$.

The equation of the tangent is

$$y - \dfrac{8}{a} = -\dfrac{8}{a^2}(x - a)$$

or $8x + a^2 y = 16a$.

The tangent has x-intercept $2a$ and y-intercept $\dfrac{-16}{a}$. Hence the coordinates of C and D are $(2a, 0)$ and $\left(0, \dfrac{16}{a}\right)$, respectively.

The midpoint of segment CD is $\left(a, \dfrac{8}{a}\right)$, or point P.

8. *Solution*

The first three pieces of information give asymptotes and two specific points. The fact that $f'(x) < 0$ for $x > 4$ tells us that the graph is strictly decreasing for $x > 4$, and could be either concave up or concave down. However, since there is no information given about points of inflection, the simplest graph is concave up for $x > 4$.

The next piece of information, $f''(x) < 0$ for $x < -1$ requires that the graph be

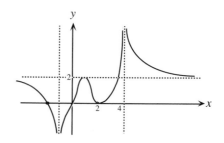

concave down in this area, that it approach asymptotes $x = -1$ and $y = 2$, and that it pass through the point $(-2, 0)$. The graph is now easily sketched.

9.   *Solution*

(i)   For local extrema, set $\dfrac{dy}{dx} = 0$.

$$\frac{1}{y}\frac{dy}{dx} = -\frac{8}{x^2} + \frac{4}{x}$$

$$\frac{dy}{dx} = y\left(\frac{4}{x} - \frac{8}{x^2}\right).$$

Since x, $y > 0$, $\dfrac{dy}{dx} = 0$ only when $x = 2$.

Also, $\dfrac{dy}{dx} < 0$ for $x < 2$ and $\dfrac{dy}{dx} > 0$ for $x > 2$.

Hence, at $x = 2$, there is a local minimum.

If $x = 2$, $\ln y = \dfrac{8}{2} + 4\ln 2 - 3$

$$= 1 + 4\ln 2$$

$$\doteq 3.77.$$

Therefore $y \doteq 43.5$.

The local minimum is at the point $(2, 43.5)$.

(ii)   When $x = 1$, $\ln y = 8 + 4\ln 1 - 3 = 5$, so $y \doteq 1.6$.

At $(1, 1.6)$, $\dfrac{dy}{dx} = 1.6(4 - 8) = -6.4$.

The equation of the tangent at $(1, 1.6)$ is

$$y - 1.6 = -6.4(x - 1)$$

or $y = -6.4x + 8$.

10.   *Solution*

Let P be the point $\left(a, a^3\right)$, since P is on the curve with

equation $y = x^3$.

For $y = x^3$, $\dfrac{dy}{dx} = 3x^2$.

Hence at P the slope of the tangent is $3a^2$, and the equation of the tangent is

$$y - a^3 = 3a^2(x - a)$$

or $y = 3a^2x - 2a^3$.

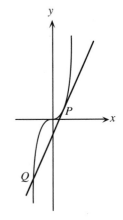

This tangent cuts the curve again at Q. We determine Q's coordinates by solving the tangent equation with $y = x^3$, obtaining

$$3a^2x - 2a^3 = x^3$$
$$x^3 - 3a^2x + 2a^2 = 0.$$

This cubic has three roots, and $x = a$ is a double root since the line is tangent at P. Since the product of the three roots is $-2a^3$, the third root is $-2a$. Hence Q has an x-coordinate of $-2a$. The slope of the curve at Q is $3(2a)^2 = 12a^2$. This is four times that of the tangent at P.

11. *Solution*
    Let BC be x metres and CD be y metres.

    Then the length of arc AED is $\frac{1}{2}\pi x$.

    The area of the window is $xy + \frac{1}{2}\pi\left(\frac{x}{2}\right)^2$.

    Since the window area is 16,

    $$xy + \frac{1}{8}\pi x^2 = 16$$
    $$y = \frac{16}{x} - \frac{\pi x}{8}.$$

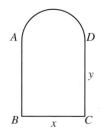

    The cost of the frame as a function of x is

    $$C(x) = 8x + 16y + 20\left(\frac{1}{2}\pi x\right)$$
    $$= 8x + 16\left(\frac{16}{x} - \frac{\pi x}{8}\right) + 10\pi x$$
    $$= 8(1 + \pi)x + \frac{256}{x}, \text{ with } x > 0.$$

    For extreme values of the function, set $C'(x) = 0$.

    $$8(1 + \pi) - \frac{256}{x^2} = 0$$
    $$x^2 = \frac{32}{1 + \pi}$$
    $$x = \sqrt{\frac{32}{1 + \pi}}, \text{ since } x > 0.$$

Hence $BC = \sqrt{\frac{32}{1 + \pi}}$ metres will minimize the cost of the framing.

12. *Solution*

Area of $C_1 = \pi\left[(x-1)^2 + 1\right] = \pi\left(x^2 - 2x + 2\right)$.

Area of $C_2 = \pi\left(x^2 + 1\right)$.

$$R(x) = \frac{x^2 - 2x + 2}{x^2 + 1}, \; x \geq 0.$$

Since $R(x)$ is continuous for $x \geq 0$, extrema occur at
points where $R'(x) = 0$, where $x = 0$, or where
$R'(x)$ does not exist. One should also examine
$R(x)$ as $x \to +\infty$.

$$R'(x) = \frac{\left(x^2 + 1\right)(2x - 2) - \left(x^2 - 2x + 2\right)(2x)}{\left(x^2 + 1\right)^2}$$

$$= \frac{2\left(x^2 - x - 1\right)}{\left(x^2 + 1\right)^2}, \text{ which exists for all } x \geq 0.$$

Setting $R'(x) = 0$ we get $x^2 - x - 1 = 0$

$$x = \frac{1 \pm \sqrt{5}}{2}.$$

Of these two values, only $x = \dfrac{1 + \sqrt{5}}{2}$ is acceptable, since $\dfrac{1 - \sqrt{5}}{2} < 0$.

$$R\left(\frac{1 + \sqrt{5}}{2}\right) = \frac{\left(\dfrac{1 + \sqrt{5}}{2}\right)^2 - 2\left(\dfrac{1 + \sqrt{5}}{2}\right) + 2}{\left(\dfrac{1 + \sqrt{5}}{2}\right)^2 + 1}$$

$$= \frac{10 - 2\sqrt{5}}{10 + 2\sqrt{5}}$$

$$= \frac{3 - \sqrt{5}}{2}. \qquad \text{(approximately 0.38)}$$

$R(0) = 2$.

$$\lim_{x \to +\infty} R(x) = \lim_{x \to +\infty} \frac{x^2 - 2x + 2}{x^2 + 1} = 1.$$

We conclude that $R(x)$ is a maximum for $x = 0$ and is a minimum for $x = \dfrac{1 + \sqrt{5}}{2}$.

13. *Solution*

(a) $\lim\limits_{\theta \to \pi} a = b+c$, since when $\theta = \pi$ the triangle

becomes the line of length $b+c$.

$\lim\limits_{\theta \to 0} a = c-b$, since when $\theta = 0$ the triangle

becomes the line of length c, and $a = c-b$.

(b) Using the Law of Cosines,

$$a^2 = b^2 + c^2 - 2bc \cos\theta.$$

Differentiating with respect to θ and noting that a is variable but b and c are fixed constants,

$$2a\frac{da}{d\theta} = 2bc \sin\theta$$

$$\frac{da}{d\theta} = \frac{bc}{a} \sin\theta.$$

Since h is the height of the triangle, we can determine a relation involving it from the area of the triangle, which can be determined in two ways.

$$\text{Area} = \frac{1}{2}ah \quad \text{or} \quad \text{area} = \frac{1}{2}bc \sin\theta$$

Then $\frac{1}{2}ah = \frac{1}{2}bc \sin\theta$

$$h = \frac{bc}{a} \sin\theta.$$

Hence $\frac{da}{d\theta} = h.$

14. *Solution*
     (i)   The x- and y-intercepts are both 4.

     (ii) $f'(x) = (4-x)e^x - e^x = e^x(3-x)$
           For a local maximum set $f'(x) = 0$.
           $e^x(3-x) = 0$.
           Since $e^x \neq 0$, $f'(x) = 0$ for $x = 3$.
           $f(3) = (4-3)e^3 \doteq 20$.
           The only local maximum is at $(3, 20)$.

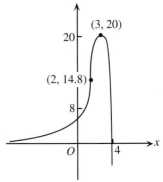

     (iii) $f''(x) = (3-x)e^x - e^x = e^x(2-x)$
           $f''(2) = 0$.
           Furthermore, for $x < 2$, $f''(x) > 0$ so the
           graph is concave up for $x < 2$.
           For $x > 2$, $f''(x) < 0$ so the graph is concave down for $x > 2$.
           Hence the only point of inflection occurs at $(2, f(2)) \doteq (2, 14.8)$.
     Comment: Why is the x-axis a horizontal asymptote?

15. *Solution*
     Represent the length of the shadow by s, the
     distance from the base of the light to the man as y
     and the distance the man is from a point T opposite
     the light as x.
     From similar triangles we have

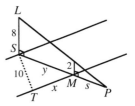

$$\frac{y+s}{s} = \frac{8}{2}$$

$$y + s = 4s$$

$$y = 3s.$$

     From the right triangle STM, $y^2 = x^2 + 10^2$.
     Therefore $9s^2 = x^2 + 10^2$.

     When $x = 10$, $9s^2 = 200$ and $s = \dfrac{10\sqrt{2}}{3}$ since $s > 0$.
     Differentiating with respect to time, $18s\dfrac{ds}{dt} = 2x\dfrac{dx}{dt}$.

     It is given that $\dfrac{dx}{dt} = \dfrac{3}{2}$.

Hence $9\left(\dfrac{10\sqrt{2}}{3}\right)\dfrac{ds}{dt}=10\left(\dfrac{3}{2}\right)$

$$30\sqrt{2}\,\dfrac{ds}{dt}=15$$

$$\dfrac{ds}{dt}=\dfrac{1}{2\sqrt{2}}.$$

The mans shadow is lengthening at $\dfrac{1}{2\sqrt{2}}$ m/s when he is 10 metres past T.

16. *Solution*

Let $\angle AOC = \theta$. Since the radius is 25 m, the length of arc AB is 25θ and $\angle COB = \pi - \theta$.
Draw $OK \perp BC$. Then $CK = BK$ and

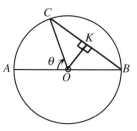

$$\angle COK = \angle KOB = \dfrac{\pi - \theta}{2}$$

$$=\dfrac{\pi}{2}-\dfrac{\theta}{2}.$$

In $\triangle OBK$, $\sin \angle KOB = \dfrac{BK}{OB}$

$$\sin\left(\dfrac{\pi}{2}-\dfrac{\theta}{2}\right)=\dfrac{BK}{25}$$

$$BK = 25\cos\dfrac{\theta}{2}.$$

The length of CB is $50\cos\dfrac{\theta}{2}$.

The time it takes to run from A to C at 4 m/s is $\dfrac{25}{4}\theta$ seconds.

The time it takes to swim from C to B at 2 m/s is $\dfrac{50\cos\dfrac{\theta}{2}}{2}=25\cos\left(\dfrac{\theta}{2}\right)$ seconds.

Hence the total time is $t = \dfrac{25}{4}\theta + 25\cos\dfrac{\theta}{2}$.

$$\dfrac{dt}{d\theta}=\dfrac{25}{4}-\dfrac{25}{2}\sin\dfrac{\theta}{2}.$$

For local maximum or minimum $\dfrac{dt}{d\theta} = 0$

$$\frac{25}{4} - \frac{25}{2} \sin \frac{\theta}{2} = 0$$

$$\sin \frac{\theta}{2} = \frac{1}{2}.$$

$$\frac{\theta}{2} = \frac{\pi}{6} \quad \text{or} \quad \frac{\theta}{2} = \frac{5\pi}{6}$$

and $\qquad \theta = \dfrac{\pi}{3} \quad \text{or} \quad \theta = \dfrac{5\pi}{3}.$

But $0 \le \theta \le \pi$, so $\theta = \dfrac{\pi}{3}$.

$$\frac{d^2t}{d\theta^2} = -\frac{25}{4} \cos \frac{\theta}{2}$$

When $\theta = \dfrac{\pi}{3}$, $\dfrac{d^2t}{d\theta^2} < 0$. Therefore $\theta = \dfrac{\pi}{3}$ yields a maximum.

Since the minimum does not occur at a critical point it must occur at an endpoint of the function.

Now, for $\theta = 0$, $t = 25$.

For $\theta = \pi$, $t = \dfrac{25\pi}{4}$

$\qquad \doteq 19.6.$

For $\theta = \dfrac{\pi}{3}$, $t = \dfrac{25}{4} \cdot \dfrac{\pi}{3} + 25 \cos \dfrac{\pi}{6}$

$\qquad \doteq 28.2.$

The minimum occurs when $\theta = \pi$ and the man runs around the pool from A to B.

17. *Solution*

In the diagram, O is the viewers eye, AB is the height of the billboard, and BC is the distance below the billboard to the horizontal through O.
We have $CB = 18$, $BA = 6$ and $\angle AOB = \theta$.
Let the distance $OC = x$, and let $\angle BOC = \alpha$.
From $\triangle AOC$, $\tan(\theta + \alpha) = \dfrac{24}{x}$, and from $\triangle BOC$,

$\tan \alpha = \dfrac{18}{x}.$

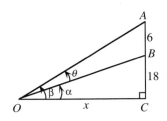

Now $\tan(\theta + \alpha) = \dfrac{\tan\theta + \tan\alpha}{1 - \tan\theta\tan\alpha} = \dfrac{24}{x}$

$$\dfrac{\tan\theta + \dfrac{18}{x}}{1 - \dfrac{18}{x}\tan\theta} = \dfrac{24}{x}$$

$$\dfrac{x\tan\theta + 18}{x - 18\tan\theta} = \dfrac{24}{x}$$

$$\tan\theta = \dfrac{6x}{x^2 + 432}. \qquad (1)$$

For extreme values we determine $\dfrac{d\theta}{dx}$ and let $\dfrac{d\theta}{dx} = 0$.

Differentiate (1) with respect to x

$$\sec^2\theta\,\dfrac{d\theta}{dx} = \dfrac{\left(x^2 + 432\right)\cdot 6 - 6x(2x)}{\left(x^2 + 432\right)^2}$$

$$= \dfrac{6x^2 + 2592 - 12x^2}{\left(x^2 + 432\right)^2}$$

$$= \dfrac{2592 - 6x^2}{\left(x^2 + 432\right)^2}.$$

Since $\sec^2\theta > 0$ it follows that $\dfrac{d\theta}{dx} = 0$ only if

$$2592 - 6x^2 = 0$$

$$x^2 = 432$$

$$x = 12\sqrt{3},\ x > 0$$

$$x \doteq 20.78.$$

Testing values of x on either side of 20.78, $\dfrac{d\theta}{dx} > 0$ for $x = 20$ and $\dfrac{d\theta}{dx} < 0$ for $x = 21$ so

θ is maximal when $x = 12\sqrt{3}$.

The viewer should stand at approximately 20.78 m to get the best view of the billboard.

Chapter 8
Answers for Exercises

1. Blaise Pascal (1623 - 1662) was a French mathematician and philosopher. The Triangle may have been linked to his name because he was interested in gambling and the numbers in the triangle count the number of ways certain hands in cards can appear. However, the Triangle was undoubtedly known before Pascal's time.

2. 1, 8, 28, 56, 70, 56, 28, 8, 1; 1, 9, 36, 84, 126, 84, 36, 9, 1.

3. Put 1's at each end of row. Any other number is the sum of the two numbers closest to it in the row above.

4. In the last list every item appears twice. Since there is no effective difference between *ch* and *hc*, etc., we need to halve the count.

    The reason the 3×2 method went wrong was that it too forgot that the choices provided for possible repetitions.

5. $(4 \times 3) \div 2 = 6$.

6. $(4 \times 3) \div 6 = 4$. It seems strange that there is less choice with three items than with two. And why did I divide by 6 this time?

7. (i) $\dfrac{3!}{2!1!} = 3$;   (ii) $\dfrac{4!}{2!2!} = 6$;   (iii) $\dfrac{10!}{6!4!} = \dfrac{10 \cdot 9 \cdot 8 \cdot 7}{4 \cdot 3 \cdot 2 \cdot 1} = 210$.

8. It's not immediately obvious how to do this Exercise. Guess and check may be as efficient a method as any. I quickly see that $\binom{n}{1} = n$, so it's easy to find one solution. For all three questions I have given two answers. Are there any more?

    (i) $n = 56$, $r = 1$ (or 55); $n = 8$, $r = 3$ (or 5);
    (ii) $n = 126$, $r = 1$ (or 125); $n = 9$, $r = 4$ (or 5);
    (iii) $n = 462$, $r = 1$ (or 461); $n = 11$, $r = 5$ (or 6).

9. $\dbinom{n}{r} = \dfrac{n!}{r!(n-r)!} = \dfrac{n!}{(n-r)!r!} = \dbinom{n}{n-r}$.

10. This should remind you of Exercise 3.

$$\binom{n}{r} + \binom{n}{r-1} = \frac{n!}{r!(n-r)!} + \frac{n!}{(r-1)!(n-r+1)!}$$

$$= \frac{n!}{(r-1)!(n-r)!}\left[\frac{1}{r} + \frac{1}{n-r+1}\right]$$

$$= \frac{(n+1)!}{r!(n-r+1)!}$$

$$= \binom{n+1}{r}.$$

11. There's a fair bit of work in doing it, but the implication is that $s = r$ or $n - r$. Can you justify it?

12. Let's assume that $n > m$. (If $n = m$, then we are finished by the last Exercise.)
So let $n = m + q$. Now go to the definition and see what happens. What happened to me was that it got quite confusing. Oh dear!

13. This should be straightforward checking.

14. This is the Binomial Theorem. I state and prove it in the next piece of text.

15. See Exercise 9.

16. It looks like 2^n in the n-th row. Why should that be?

17. The coefficients of $(x+y)^6$ can be found from Figure 1. The rest is just a check.

18. $(x-y)^6 = x^6 - 6x^5y + 15x^4y^2 - 20x^3y^3 + 15x^2y^4 - 6xy^5 + y^6$

19. $(x+2y)^5 = \sum_{r=0}^{5}\binom{5}{r}x^{5-r}(2y)^r$

$$= x^5 + 10x^4y + 40x^3y^2 + 80x^2y^3 + 80xy^4 + 32y^5.$$

20. $(x+y)^n = \sum_{r=0}^{n} \binom{n}{r} x^{n-r} y^r$

Let $x = 1 = y$. Then $(1+1)^n = \sum_{r=0}^{n} \binom{n}{r} 1^{n-r} 1^r$, so $\sum_{r=0}^{n} \binom{n}{r} = 2^n$.

[Aha, see exercise 16!]

21. (a)   Did you get 16? (That looks astonishingly like 2^4 to me.)

(b)   I'm too lazy to write them all down. Did you get 243?

(c)   Surely with m letters we can make m^n words of length n.

22. Multiply $(A+B)^3$ out without using the commutative law, that is, don't assume that $AB = BA$. You should then see all the words come tripping out.

23. 8. What a surprise!

24. $(A+B+C)^4 = A^4 + 4\left(A^3B + A^3C + AB^3 + AC^3 + B^3C + BC^3\right)$

$$+ 6\left(A^2B^2 + A^2C^2 + B^2C^2\right) + 12\left(A^2BC + AB^2C + ABC^2\right)$$

$$+ \cdots$$

As for the coefficient of AB^2C, the answer is 12. Did you get it.

25. $(x+y+z)^n = \sum \dfrac{n!}{r_1! r_2! r_3!} x^{r_1} y^{r_2} z^{r_3}$, where $r_1 + r_2 + r_3 = n$, and the summation is over all r_1, r_2, r_3 which sum to n.

26. Sequences of 15 ones and 2 zeros? No worries. That's $\binom{17}{2} = \dfrac{17!}{2!15!} = \dfrac{17 \cdot 16}{2} = 136$.

27. I couldn't get 136 somehow.

28. I'll need 22 ones and 3 zeros. This'll give $\binom{25}{3} = \dfrac{25 \cdot 24 \cdot 23}{3!} = 230$.

29. Ah now! **Positive** it is that you want! Suppose I change the equation by putting $x = X+1$. Then, when I get a solution $X = 0$, I'll find $x = 1$, so x will never be zero. (It will also never be negative if I insist that X is non-negative.) So it looks like I'll replace x by $X+1$, y by $Y+1$ and z by $Z+1$. Therefore $X+Y+Z = 12$.

This has $\binom{14}{2} = \dfrac{14 \cdot 13}{2} = 91$ solutions (including zero ones). So $x+y+z = 15$ has 91 solutions, none of which is zero.

30. Let $x = X+3$, $y = Y+4$, $z = Z+5$. Repeat the above and you'll get $\binom{5}{2} = \dfrac{5 \cdot 4}{2} = 10$

solutions. There are 10 solutions for x, y, z of the desired type.

Solutions to Problems

1. *Solution*

The coefficients of x^5 is $\binom{n}{5}$ and the coefficient of x^{15} is $\binom{n}{15}$. If $\binom{n}{5} = \binom{n}{15}$, then

$n = 20$.

2. *Solution*

The only terms in $f(x)$ containing x^{98} are $(1+x)^{98}$, $(1+x)^{99}$ and $(1+x)^{100}$.

In $(1+x)^{98}$, the coefficient of x^{98} is 1.

In $(1+x)^{99}$, the coefficient of x^{98} is $\binom{99}{98}$ or $\binom{99}{1}$.

In $(1+x)^{100}$, the coefficient of x^{98} is $\binom{100}{98}$ or $\binom{100}{2}$.

The coefficient of x^{98} in $f(x)$ is $1 + \binom{99}{1} + \binom{100}{2}$.

If simplified, this equals 5050.

3. *Solution*

There are 9 single-digit integers $1, 2, \cdots, 9$.

There are 90 two-digit integers $10, 11, \cdots, 99$, using 180 digits.

There are $n - 99$ three-digit numbers (if n is itself a three-digit number), using $3(n-99)$ digits.

Hence $3(n-99) = 2400$

$$n - 99 = 800$$
$$n = 899.$$

4. *Solution*

(a) We note that $7777 = 7 \times 1111$

$$= 7 \times 11 \times 101.$$

The only possibilities for the two numbers are 77×101 and 11×707.

Therefore the largest three-digit number is 707.

(b)   Let N be the smallest multiple of 49 which has all of its digits the same.
      Then $N = k + 10k + 100k + 1000k + \cdots$

$$= k(1111\ldots).$$

Now, $k(1111\ldots)$ must be divisible by 49, so we want $k = 7$ and $111\ldots1$ to be divisible by 7, unless the first string of 1's that is divisible by 7 is also divisible by 49, in which case $k = 1$.

We divide 7 into 11, 111, 1111, etc., until we find a remainder of 0; i.e., $111111 = 7(15\,873)$, and 7 does not divide $15\,873$.

Hence $7(7)(15\,873) = 7(111111) = 777\,777$ is the smallest multiple of 49 which has all of its digits the same.

5.   *Solution*

There are three choices for t_1, three for t_2, and three for t_3.

Therefore, there are $3 \times 3 \times 3 = 27$ possible sequences.

The five arithmetic sequences satisfying the requirements are $(1, 4, 7)$, $(2, 5, 8)$, $(3, 6, 9)$, $(1, 5, 9)$, and $(3, 5, 7)$.

Therefore the probability that t_1, t_2, t_3 is an arithmetic sequence is $\frac{5}{27}$.

6.   *Solution*

From 10 to 19, there will be 8 increases.

From 20 to 29, there will be 7 increases.

From 30 to 39, there will be 6 increases.

$\ldots$

From 90 to 99, there will be 0 increases.

Therefore, when the order of the digits is reversed, there will be

$8 + 7 + 6 + 5 + 4 + 3 + 2 + 1 = 36$ numbers in the set.

7.   *Solution*

[Note: Do the last digit first because it overlaps, possibly, with the first.]

There are two cases: last digit 1 or 3, or else last digit 2 or 4.

If the last digit is 1 or 3, there are 2 choices for it.

There are then 4 choices for the first digit and 7! for the remaining 7 positions.

Hence there are $2 \times 4 \times 7!$ permutations.

If the last digit is 2 or 4, there are 2 choices for it, 5 choices for the first digit, and 7! choices for the remaining digits.

There are $8 \times 7! + 10 \times 7!$ or $18 \times 7!$ permutations.

8.   *Solution*

We can write $332 = k_1 d + r$ (1)

               $520 = k_2 d + r$ (2)

and $755 = k_3 d + r$ (3)   for some positive integers k_1, k_2, k_3.

(2) – (1) gives $(k_2 - k_1)d = 188 = 4 \times 47$.

$(3) - (2)$ gives $(k_3 - k_2)d = 235 = 5 \times 47$.

Since d is a factor of the left sides, it must be a factor of the right side.

Hence $d = 47$, since $d > 1$.

Since $332 = 7(47) + 3$, then $r = 3$.

Therefore, $d + r = 47 + 3 = 50$.

9. *Solution*

There are 4! arrangements of the French books, 6! arrangements of the Spanish books, and 7! arrangements of the German books.

We must also order the languages, and there are 3! ways of doing this.

There are, then, 4!6!7!3! ways of arranging the books.

10. *Solution*

There are 6! arrangements of the letters.

(a) If a and b are side by side, consider them as one that can be writtem either as ab or ba.

There are 2.5! arrangements of the five letters.

The probability of a and b together is $\dfrac{2.5!}{6!} = \dfrac{1}{3}$.

(b) Every arrangement has either a ahead of b or else b ahead of a. Since these are equally likely to happen, the probability that a is ahead of b is $\dfrac{1}{2}$.

[You can, of course, count the ways by putting a in the first position, with 5 places for b and 4! for the others, or a in the second position with 4 places for b and 4! for the others, etc.]

11. *Solution*

An odd perfect square occurs when an odd integer is squared.

Any odd integer is of the form $2n + 1$, where n is an integer.

Now, $(2n + 1)^2 = 4n^2 + 4n + 1$

$$= 4\left(n^2 + n\right) + 1$$

$$= 4n(n + 1) + 1.$$

But $n(n + 1)$ is the product of two consecutive integers, one of which must be even.

Thus $n(n + 1)$ is of the form $2k$, where k is an integer.

Hence, $(2n + 1)^2 = 4(2k) + 1 = 8k + 1$.

Therefore any odd perfect square can be written in the form $8k + 1$, for some integer k.

12. *Solution*
    (a) There are 7 possible last digits, of which 4 are odd. The arrangement of the other digits is immaterial in determining whether the number is odd or even.

    The probability that the number is odd is $\frac{4}{7}$.

    (b) The number is less than 3 200 000 if

    (i) the first digit is 1 or 2, which happens with probability $\frac{2}{7}$, or

    (ii) the first digit is 3 and the second digit is 1, which happens with probability $\frac{1}{7} \times \frac{1}{6} = \frac{1}{42}$.

    Hence the probability is $\frac{2}{7} + \frac{1}{42} = \frac{13}{42}$.

    (c) A number is divisible by 4 if the final two digits are divisible by 4. There are two such cases:

    (i) if the number ends in 24 or 64. This happens with probability $\frac{1}{7} \times \frac{2}{6} = \frac{1}{21}$.

    (ii) if the number ends in 2 or 6 and the second last digit is odd. This happens with probability $\frac{2}{7} \times \frac{4}{6} = \frac{4}{21}$.

    The total probability, since these are independent events, is $\frac{1}{21} + \frac{4}{21} = \frac{5}{21}$.

13. *Solution*
    [Note: We first select three students to receive two books each. We'll then give them their books.]

    Three students, each of whom will receive two books, can be chosen in $\binom{6}{3}$ ways.

    [Note: Does their order matter?]

    The first of these students can be given two different books in $\binom{9}{2}$ ways. The second can be given two different books in $\binom{7}{2}$ ways, because there are seven books left. The third can be given two books in $\binom{5}{2}$ ways. The remaining books can be given to the other students in 3! ways.

    The number of distributions is $\binom{6}{3}\binom{9}{2}\binom{7}{2}\binom{5}{2}3!$

    [Note: This is a perfectly acceptable answer. Some people like things worked out. If so, you can simplify this answer to $\frac{9!}{2!2!2!}\binom{6}{3}$. Can you interpret this?]

14.   *Solution*

There are $2^5 = 32$ possible outcomes since every coin has two sides. Of these the only ones not meeting the requirement have no head or exactly one head. There is only one way in the first case and there are 5 ways in the second case since any one of the five coins could have its head showing. Hence the probability is $\dfrac{32-(1+5)}{32} = \dfrac{13}{16}$.

15.   *Solution*

Represent each of the 5 volumes chosen by an a and each of the remaining 15 volumes not chosen by a b.

Then each of the arrangements of 5 a's and 15 b's represents an acceptable selection provided that there are no adjacent a's.

Such a selection is obtained by choosing 5 of the 16 (one at each end and fourteen gaps) open spaces determined by the 15 b's.

There are $\dbinom{16}{5}$ possible selections.

16.   *Solution*

Let the length of the hypotenuse be $10x + y$, where x is the tens digit $(1 \le x \le 9)$ and y is the units digit $(1 \le y \le 9)$, and where $x > y$.

Therefore, another side has length $10y + x$.

If the third side has length a, then by the Pythagorean Theorem,

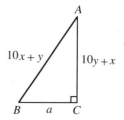

$$a^2 = (10x + y)^2 - (10y + x)^2$$
$$= 100x^2 + 20xy + y^2 - 100y^2 - 20xy - x^2$$
$$= 99\left(x^2 - y^2\right)$$
$$= 9(11)\left(x^2 - y^2\right).$$

Therefore $11\left(x^2 - y^2\right)$ must be a perfect square, and so $x^2 - y^2 = 11k^2$, where k is an integer.

Thus $(x + y)(x - y) = 11k^2$.

Since $1 < x - y < 9$, where $1 \le x \le 9, 1 \le y \le 9$, it follows that 11 is a divisor of $x + y$ and we must have $x + y = 11m$ for some integer m.

But $x + y \le 18$, so that $x + y = 11$.

Since $x > y$, the smallest possible value of x is 6.

In this case, $y = 5$, leading to the smallest possible length of 65 for the hypotenuse.

17. *Solution*

Omitting the B's, there are 3 A's, 2 C's, 2 D's to arrange, and there are $\dfrac{7!}{3!\,2!\,2!}$

arrangements.

There are 8 spaces in which to insert the three B's, and three spaces can be chosen in $\dbinom{8}{3}$

ways.

The total number of arrangements is $\dfrac{7!}{3!\,2!\,2!}\dbinom{8}{3}$.

18. *Solution*

(a) In order that the product of the digits in all sets of five consecutive positions be divisible by 5, the digit 5 must be in the fourth of fifth position. The remaining seven digits can be in any of the other positions. Hence here are $2 \times 7!$ permutations with the restriction.

(b) To meet the requirement of every pair of consecutive digits having even product we require that no two odd digits by adjacent. There are 5 possible positions separated by even digits and 4 must be chosen in which to locate the odd digits.

The total number is then $\dbinom{5}{4}(4!)^2$ or $5 \times (4!)^2$.

19. *Solution*

(a) Each position can be filled in two ways, either with an H or a T. Hence there are 2^n possible sequences.

(b) There is no HT in the sequence only if the sequence is of the form $T \cdots TH \cdots H$, where there are k T's and $(n-k)H$'s. Then k can be any integer value chosen from 0, 1, 2, ..., n. Hence there are $n+1$ such sequences.

Solution 1

(c) If there is exactly one occurrence of HT, the sequence must be of the form $T \cdots TH \cdots HT \cdots TH \cdots H$. There are k T's in the first block and $0 \le k \le n-2$. There are l H's in the second block and $1 \le l \le n-1$. There are m T's in the third block and $2 \le m < n$. There are then $\left[n - (k+l+m)\right]$ H's in the final block. This is equivalent to $0 \le k < (k+l) < (k+l+m) \le n$. Considering k, $(k+l)$, $(k+l+m)$, as three integers, this is equivalent to selecting three integers from the set 0, 1, 2, ..., n which can be done in $\dbinom{n+1}{3}$ ways, and this is the number of sequences possible.

Solution 2

As in solution 1 the sequence must be of the form $T \cdots TH \cdots HT \cdots TH \cdots H$. Hence there are two strings as in part (b) of length k and $n - k$, with $1 \le k \le n - 1$, since there must be at least one H in string one and at least one T in string two. Then there are k possible strings for the first part and $n - k$ possible strings for the second part. Since any of the possible first strings can be matched with any of the possible second strings there are, for any value of k, $k(n - k)$ possible sequences. The total number of sequences, then, is

$$\sum_{k=1}^{n-1} k(n-k) = n \sum_{k=1}^{n-1} k - \sum_{k=1}^{n-1} k^2$$

$$= n \frac{n(n-1)}{2} - \frac{(n-1)(n)(2n-1)}{6}$$

$$= \frac{(n-1)(n)(n+1)}{6}$$

$$= \binom{n+1}{3}.$$

There are $\binom{n+1}{3}$ possible sequences.

20. *Solution 1*

We may proceed by grouping $a + b$ and $c + d$ as terms then expanding as a binomial.

$$(a+b+c+d)^{10} = (a+b)^{10}$$

$$+ \binom{10}{1}(a+b)^9(c+d)$$

$$+ \binom{10}{2}(a+b)^8(c+d)^2$$

$$+ \cdots + \binom{10}{10}(c+d)^{10}.$$

The total number of terms will be the sum of the terms generated by each expansion.

i.e. $(a+b)^{10}$ contributes 11 terms

$(a+b)^9(c+d)$ contributes 10×2 terms

$(a+b)^8(c+d)^2$ contributes 9×3 terms

$$\vdots$$

$(c+d)^{10}$ contributes 11 terms.

The sum of the above can be expressed as

$$\sum_{k=1}^{11} k(12-k) = 12 \sum_{k=1}^{11} k - \sum_{k=1}^{11} k^2 .$$

But $\displaystyle\sum_{k=1}^{n} k = \frac{n(n+1)}{2}$ and $\displaystyle\sum_{k=1}^{n} k^2 = \frac{n(n+1)(2n+1)}{6}$.

Therefore $\displaystyle\sum_{k=1}^{11} k(12-k) = \frac{12(11)(12)}{2} - \frac{11(12)(23)}{6}$

$$= \frac{12.11}{6}[36-23]$$

$$= \frac{13.12.11}{6}$$

$$= 286.$$

There are 286 terms in the expansion of $(a+b+c+d)^{10}$.

Solution 2

In the expansion of $(a+b+c+d)^{10}$ we will have ten identical sets of $a+b+c+d$ which when multiplied will generate terms of degree 10.

Consider the 10 sets as being arranged in a line: $x\ x\ x\ x\ x\ x\ x\ x\ x\ x$. Inserting 3 dividing lines in the 9 spaces between the x's will give us 4 groups with at least one x in each group. The groups in order will represent the powers of a, b, c and d. Some groups may be empty, so to facilitate our count we add 4 more sets, insert 3 dividing lines in the 13 spaces to form the 4 groups, then remove one set from each group.
A particular division is as follows

$$x \quad x \quad x\big|\,x\,\big|\,x \quad x \quad x \quad x \quad x \,\big|\,x \quad x \quad x \quad x.$$

This represents the term $a^2 c^5 d^3$.

The 3 dividing lines inserted in the 13 spaces will give us $\binom{13}{3}$ cases.

Hence there are 286 terms in the expansion of $(a+b+c+d)^{10}$.

Solution 3

We can write 4 infinite geometric series as follows:

$$1 + ax + a^2 x^2 + \dots$$
$$1 + bx + b^2 x^2 + \dots$$
$$1 + cx + c^2 x^2 + \dots$$
$$1 + dx + d^2 x^2 + \dots$$

Multiplying the four series together will give us the product

$$\left(1 + ax + a^2x^2 + ...\right)\left(1 + bx + b^2x^2 + ...\right)\left(1 + cx + c^2x^2 + ...\right)\left(1 + dx + d^2x^2 + ...\right)$$
$$= 1 + (a + b + c + d)x$$
$$+ \left(a^2 + b^2 + ... + ab + ...\right)x^2$$
$$+ \left(a^3 + b^3 + ... + a^2b + ... + abc + ...\right)x^3$$
$$+ ... \; .$$

Note that the coefficient of x^r will be made up of the product of powers of a, b, c and d to give terms of degree r. The number of terms of degree r can be established by letting $a = b = c = d = 1$ and then determining the coefficient of x^r.

When $a = b = c = d = 1$, each of the given series is $(1 - x)^{-1}$ and their product is $(1 - x)^{-4}$.

The term containing x^r is the $(r + 1)$st term.

$$t_{r+1} = \frac{(-4)(-5)(-6)...(-4 - r + 1)}{r!}(-x)^r$$

$$= (-1)^r \frac{4 \cdot 5 \cdot 6 \cdot 7 ... (r + 3)}{r!}(-1)^r x^r$$

$$= (-1)^{2r} \frac{1 \cdot 2 \cdot 3 \cdot 4 \cdot 5 \cdot ... \cdot (r + 3)}{1 \cdot 2 \cdot 3 \cdot r!} x^r$$

$$= \frac{(r + 3)!}{r! \, 3!} x^r.$$

For the expansion $(a + b + c + d)^{10}$, $r = 10$ and hence the number of terms will be

$$\frac{13!}{10! 3!} = 286.$$

Chapter 9
Answers for Exercises

1. Here's two sets that I found: $\{2, 5, 8, 11, 14, 17\}$, $\{1, 4, 6, 8, 11, 13\}$.

2. What did you find?

3. Note that the mapping $f(n) = 4n - 1$ takes $\{1, 2, 3, 4, 5, 6\}$ to $\{3, 7, 11, 15, 19, 23\}$. Hence f will also map a Mathmark to a Mathmark$^+$.

4. To get a feel for this you should check the Mathmarks$^+$ in the last Exercise. Their side sums were 33, 37, 41 and 45.

    To go from $\{1, 2, 3, 4, 5, 6\}$ to A we need a mapping of the form $f(n) = a + (n-1)d$. You might think that the side sums of Mathmarks$^+$ are $f(9)$, $f(10)$, $f(11)$, $f(12)$. However, this doesn't agree with the side sums from Exercise 3. In fact, the side sums are $3a + 6d$, $3a + 8d$, and $3a + 9d$. Why?

5. First of all, I'm assuming that a and d are both non-negative integers. (You might prefer otherwise, of course.) And since I want all of A to be different $d \geq 1$. The question then is, is there any number that can't be expressed in the form $3a + kd$ for $k = 6, 7, 8, 9$?

    Since $a \geq 0$ and $d \geq 1$, the smallest side sum I can get is 6. So it's not possible to get side sums smaller than this. But after that, $3 \times 0 + 6$, $3 \times 0 + 7$, $3 \times 0 + 8$ are consecutive. Does this remind you of an earlier problem (stamps, Chapter 1)? So you should be able to see that all side sums from 6 on are possible.

6. I guess we have some exploring to do.

7. How did you do with the proof?

8. M is nice I'm afraid. Which rather messes up the Conjecture. I'll find all possible Mathmarks$^+$. Using corners $= 3s - 22$, and $10 \leq s \leq 13$, I get sums of corners $= 8, 11, 14, 17$. But $4 + 5 + 7 = 16 < 17$. So corners $= 8, 11, 14$. Working systematically from here I form the following Mathmarks$^+$.

This is actually surprising on two counts. First of all it's the first non-arithmetic progression I've found that is nice. Second, unlike Mathmarks, there are only **two**, not **four**, Mathmarks$^+$ which come from this M.

9. No Mathmarks$^+$ here.

10. So the Conjecture is false because $\{1,2,3,4,5,7\}$ is a counterexample. Where do we go from here?

11. Apart from playing around with the current relations, I can't see how to get anything **new**. Will the old equations get me anywhere?

12. Did it help you? It didn't me.

13. Clearly from the second of equations (2), I only need a, c, d to find f.

14. Yes. Use the first two equations of (2).

15. No. Check out all possibilities.

16. If Exercise 15 is "No", then so is this one.

17. Just use the (a) to (b) argument, replacing a by f, b by a, c by b, etc.

18. I'm not quite sure yet. It does tell me though that if I can get one Mathmark$^+$ I can get another, different one.

19. How did you do?

20. I don't think we have to have c or e the second smallest. Try $a=1$, $c=101$, $e=201$ and $\beta=1$. Then $a < a+\beta < c$.

21. This is just a rewrite of the text. It turns out that a doesn't **have** to be the smallest element. Nowhere in the proof do we use this fact.

22. M only gives two Mathmarks$^+$. To get four, there have to be two possible values of β in the set.

    (Check this out with $\{1,2,3,4,5,6\}$. Is it possible to have **three** values of β?

    Does that mean that some sets have **six** Mathmarks$^+$?)

23. $\{1,2,3,4,5,7\}$: $a=1$, $c=2$, $e=5$ and $\beta=2$. This at least rules out e as the third smallest element. (See Exercise 21.)

    $\{1,2,3,4,5,8\}$: Let $a=1$. How do we get 8? If $1+\beta=8$, then β is too large for c and e. If $1+\beta=5$, then $4+\beta=8$ but $2+\beta\neq3$. Trying $1+\beta=4$, $1+\beta=3$, $1+\beta=2$ are all inadequate. So this set doesn't meet the criteria of the Theorem and so it is not nice.

24. Over to your imagination. (How about circles on the sides of squares or regular polygons?)

25. (a) You should be able to get 14, 16, 17 but no others.

    (b) This should keep you busy following the kind of track I followed with nice numbers. Good luck.

Solutions to Problems

1. *Solution*
    Let point P's rate be p cm/s and let Q's rate be q cm/s.
    If they move in opposite directions, then, in 6 seconds, P has travelled $6p$ cm and Q has travelled $6q$ cm for a sum of 360 cm.
    Hence $6p + 6q = 360$.   (1)
    If they move in the same direction, then, in 24 seconds, P has travelled $24p$ cm and Q has travelled $24q$ cm to give a difference of 360 cm.

    Hence $24p - 24q = 360$ (2)   (assuming $p > q$)
    (1) ÷ 6 gives $p + q = 60$ (3)
    (2) ÷ 24 gives $p - q = 15$ (4)
    (3) + (4) gives $2p = 75$
                         $p = 37.5$
                 and so $q = 22.5$.

    Therefore the rates at which the points move are 37.5 cm/s and 22.5 cm/s.

2. *Solution 1*
    (Neither $\angle A$ nor $\angle B$ is obtuse, since, if either was, one side of the equation $b \cos A = a \cos B$ would be positive, and the other side negative - a contradiction.

    Hence $\angle A$ and $\angle B$ are both acute.

    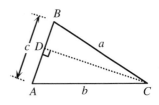

    Draw a perpendicular from C, meeting AB at D.
    Then $AD = b \cos A$ and $BD = a \cos B$.
    But we are given that $b \cos A = a \cos B$,
    so $AD = BD$.
    Therefore CD is the perpendicular bisector of AB.
    Therefore $CB = CA$ or $a = b$, since any point on the perpendicular bisector of a line segment is equidistant from the endpoints of the line segment.

Solution 2

By the Cosine Law, $a^2 = b^2 + c^2 - 2bc \cos A$ or $b \cos A = \dfrac{b^2 + c^2 - a^2}{2c}$,

and $b^2 = a^2 + c^2 - 2ac \cos B$ or $a \cos B = \dfrac{a^2 + c^2 - b^2}{2c}$.

Since $b \cos A = a \cos B$, then $b^2 + c^2 - a^2 = a^2 + c^2 - b^2$

$$b^2 - a^2 = a^2 - b^2$$
$$2a^2 = 2b^2$$
$$a^2 = b^2$$
$$a = b. \quad \text{(since } a \text{ and } b \text{ are both positive)}$$

3. *Solution 1*

$f(x) \le k^2 + 1$ if and only if $\left(k^2 + 1\right) - f(x) \ge 0$ for all x.

Consider $k^2 + 1 - f(x) = k^2 + 1 - \dfrac{(x+k)^2}{x^2 + 1}$

$$= \dfrac{\left(k^2 + 1\right)\left(x^2 + 1\right) - (x+k)^2}{x^2 + 1}$$

$$= \dfrac{k^2 x^2 - 2kx + 1}{x^2 + 1}$$

$$= \dfrac{(kx - 1)^2}{x^2 + 1} \ge 0 \quad \text{for all } x.$$

Hence $f(x) \le k^2 + 1$.

Solution 2

$f(x) = \dfrac{(x+k)^2}{x^2 + 1}$

Suppose there exists a value of x for which $f(x) > k^2 + 1$.

Then $\qquad\qquad \dfrac{(x+k)^2}{x^2 + 1} > k^2 + 1$

$\qquad (x+k)^2 > \left(k^2 + 1\right)\left(x^2 + 1\right)$, since $x^2 + 1 > 0$

$\qquad x^2 + 2kx + k^2 > k^2 x^2 + k^2 + x^2 + 1$

$\qquad\qquad 0 > k^2 x^2 - 2kx + 1$

$\qquad\qquad 0 > (kx - 1)^2$, which is false.

Therefore such a value of x does not exist.

Therefore $f(x) \le k^2 + 1$ for all values of x.

4.   (a)   *Solution*

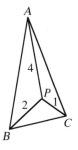

If $\angle APB = \angle BPC = \angle CPA$, then each angle
is $120°$.

Now, $(AB)^2 = (AP)^2 + (PB)^2 - 2(AP)(PB)\cos 120°$

$$= 16 + 4 - 2(4)(2)\left(-\frac{1}{2}\right)$$

$$= 28.$$

Similarly, $(AC)^2 = 16 + 1 - 2(4)(1)\left(-\frac{1}{2}\right) = 21$

and $(BC)^2 = 4 + 1 - 2(2)(1)\left(-\frac{1}{2}\right) = 7.$

Hence $(AB)^2 = (AC)^2 + (BC)^2$, and so $\angle ACB$ is a right angle.

(b)   *Solution 1*

$\triangle APB \approx \triangle BPC$ since $AP = 2BP$, $PB = 2PC$,
and $\angle APB = \angle BPC$. Hence if BC has length t, AB has length $2t$.
We are given that $\angle ACB = 90°$, so $(AC)^2 = (AB)^2 - (BC)^2 = 3t^2$, and $AC = \sqrt{3}t$.
Since $\triangle ABC$ has sides $t, 2t, \sqrt{3}t$, it has angles $30°, 60°, 90°$. Hence $\angle ABC = 60°$.
From the similar triangles, $\angle BAP = \angle PBC$.
Therefore $\angle BAP + \angle ABP = \angle PBC + \angle ABP = 60°$.
Hence $\angle APB = 120°$, and since $\angle BPC = \angle APB$, we conclude that $\angle APC = 120°$
because the sum of the angles at P is $360°$.

Solution 2

If $\angle APB$ is α, then since $\angle APB = \angle BPC$, $\angle APC$ is $2\pi - 2\alpha$.
Using the Cosine Law,

$$(AB)^2 = (AP)^2 + (PB)^2 - 2(AP)(PB)\cos \alpha = 20 - 16 \cos \alpha$$
$$(BC)^2 = (BP)^2 + (PC)^2 - 2(BP)(PC)\cos \alpha = 5 - 4 \cos \alpha$$
$$(AC)^2 = (AP)^2 + (PC)^2 - 2(AP)(PC)\cos (2\pi - 2\alpha) = 17 - 8 \cos 2\alpha.$$

Since $\angle ACB = 90°, (AB)^2 = (BC)^2 + (AC)^2.$
Hence, $20 - 16 \cos \alpha = 5 - 4 \cos \alpha + 17 - 8 \cos 2\alpha$
$8 \cos 2\alpha - 12 \cos \alpha - 2 = 0.$
Using $\cos 2\alpha = 2 \cos^2 a - 1$, we get

$$8 \cos^2 \alpha - 6 \cos \alpha - 5 = 0$$
$$(4 \cos \alpha - 5)(2 \cos \alpha + 1) = 0$$
$$\cos \alpha = \frac{5}{4} \text{ or } \cos \alpha = -\frac{1}{2}.$$

But $\cos \alpha \neq \frac{5}{4}$ since $|\cos \alpha| \leq 1$.

Therefore $\cos \alpha = -\frac{1}{2}$ and $\alpha = 120°$.
Hence $\angle APC = 120°$.

5.   *Solution*
      (a)   Suppose that every term of the sequence is divisible by some prime p.
            Then the difference between any two terms is divisible by p.

            For example, $a_{n+1} - a_n = \left(2^{n+1}k + 1\right) - \left(2^n k + 1\right)$

            $$= 2^n k \text{ is also divisible by } p.$$

            But, $2^n k$ and $2^n k + 1$ are consecutive integers, and cannot both be divisible by p.
            Therefore we have a contradiction, and so there is no prime, p, dividing every term.

      (b)   Suppose that p and q are primes so that each term of the sequence is divisible by
            either p or q.
            As in part (a), neither p nor q can divide consecutive terms.
            Therefore if p divides a_n, q must divide a_{n+1}, p must divide a_{n+2}, q must divide
            a_{n+3}, and so on.
            If p divides a_n and a_{n+2}, then it also divides

            $$a_{n+2} - a_n = \left(2^{n+2}k + 1\right) - \left(2^n k + 1\right)$$

            $$= 2^n k(4 - 1)$$

            $$= 3 \cdot 2^n k.$$

            Since p divides $2^n k + 1$, it cannot divide $2^n k$ (since they are consecutive integers)
            and since p divides $3 \cdot 2^n k$, then p must divide 3.
            Hence $p = 3$.
            Also, since q divides a_{n+1} and a_{n+3}, it must also divide

            $$a_{n+3} - a_{n+1} = \left(2^{n+3}k + 1\right) - \left(2^{n+1}k + 1\right)$$

            $$= 2^{n+1}k(4 - 1)$$

            $$= 3 \cdot 2^{n+1}k.$$

            Since q divides $2^{n+1}k + 1$, it cannot divide $2^{n+1}k$ and so q divides 3.
            Hence $q = 3$.
            But $p \neq q$, and so we have a contradiction.
            Therefore there are no two primes p and q such that each term for the sequence is
            divisible by either p or q.

6. *Solution 1*

Let $z = |x - 3|$.

Then the equation becomes

$$y = 6z^2 - 4z + 3$$

$$= 6\left(z^2 - \frac{2}{3}z + \frac{1}{9} - \frac{1}{9}\right) + 3$$

$$= 6\left(z - \frac{1}{3}\right)^2 + \frac{7}{3}.$$

The value of y is minimized when $z = \frac{1}{3}$.

That is, $|x - 3| = \frac{1}{3}$

$$x - 3 = \frac{1}{3} \quad \text{or} \quad x - 3 = -\frac{1}{3}$$

$$x = \frac{10}{3} \quad \text{or} \qquad x = \frac{8}{3}.$$

The minimum value of y is $\frac{7}{3}$, when $x = \frac{8}{3}$ or $x = \frac{10}{3}$.

Solution 2

If $x \geq 3, |x - 3| = x - 3$ and the given equation becomes

$$y = 6(x - 3)^2 - 4(x - 3) + 3$$

$$= 6x^2 - 40x + 69$$

$$= 6\left(x^2 - \frac{20}{3}x + \frac{100}{9}\right) - \frac{200}{3} + 69$$

$$= 6\left(x - \frac{10}{3}\right)^2 + \frac{7}{3}.$$

If $x < 3, |x - 3| = -(x - 3)$ and the given equation becomes

$$y = 6(x - 3)^2 + 4(x - 3) + 3$$

$$= 6\left(x - \frac{8}{3}\right)^2 + \frac{7}{3}, \text{ as above.}$$

Therefore the minimum value of y is $\frac{7}{3}$, when $x = \frac{8}{3}$ or $x = \frac{10}{3}$.

7. *Solution 1*
    Join *BD* and draw *AE* and *CF* perpendicular to
    BD, and let *BE* be *x*, *ED* be *y*, *BF* be *p*, and *FD*
    be *q*.
    By the Pythagorean Theorem

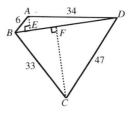

$$AE^2 = 6^2 - x^2 = 34^2 - y^2$$
$$y^2 - x^2 = 34^2 - 6^2 = 1120.$$

Also, $CF^2 = 33^2 - p^2 = 47^2 - q^2$
$$q^2 - p^2 = 47^2 - 33^2 = 1120.$$
Hence $y^2 - x^2 = q^2 - p^2$
$$(y + x)(y - x) = (q + p)(q - p).$$
Since $y + x = q + p = BD$
then $y - x = q - p$.
Adding gives $y = q$ and so $x = p$.
Thus *A*, *E*, *F* and *C* are collinear and the diagonals of *ABCD* are perpendicular.

Solution 2
Select co-ordinate axes so that *A*, *B*, and *C* lie on
the axes as illustrated. (To prove the diagonals
of *ABCD* are perpendicular we must prove
that $x = 0$.)
Using the distance formula,

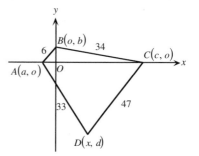

$a^2 + b^2 = 36$	(1)
$b^2 + c^2 = 1156$	(2)
$(x - a)^2 + d^2 = 1089$	(3)
$(x - c)^2 + d^2 = 2209$	(4)

(4) – (3) gives $c^2 - a^2 + 2ax - 2cx = 1120$
(2) – (1) gives $c^2 - a^2 = 1120$
Therefore $2ax - 2cx = 0$
$$x(2a - 2c) = 0.$$
But $a \neq c$.
Therefore $x = 0$.
Hence *D* lies on the *y*-axis and so *AC* and *BD* are perpendicular.

8. *Solution*

    (a) On a single roll Ann has the probability of $\frac{1}{6}$ of winning, while Bob has a

         probability of $\frac{1}{2}$ of winning on a single toss. The probability that Ann wins on her

         *k*th roll is the product of the probabilities that she loses on her first $(k - 1)$ rolls, that

         Bob loses on his first $(k - 1)$ tosses, and that Ann rolls a 6 on her *k*th roll. The

         probability that she wins the game is the sum of all possible winning probabilities.

Hence $P(\text{Ann wins}) = \frac{1}{6} + \frac{5}{6} \cdot \frac{1}{2} \cdot \frac{1}{6} + \left(\frac{5}{6} \cdot \frac{1}{2}\right)^2 \frac{1}{6} + \left(\frac{5}{6} \cdot \frac{1}{2}\right)^3 \frac{1}{6} + \cdots$

$$= \frac{1}{6}\left[1 + \frac{5}{12} + \left(\frac{5}{12}\right)^2 + \left(\frac{5}{12}\right)^3 + \cdots\right]$$

$$= \frac{1}{6}\left[\frac{1}{1 - \frac{5}{12}}\right]$$

$$= \frac{2}{7}.$$

The probability that Ann wins is $\frac{2}{7}$.

(b)   From part (a) we have $p(k) = \left(\frac{5}{6}\right)^{k-1}\left(\frac{1}{2}\right)^{k-1}\frac{1}{6} = \frac{1}{6}\left(\frac{5}{12}\right)^{k-1}$.

For Bob to win on his kth play, Ann must lose k times.

Hence $q(k) = \left(\frac{5}{6}\right)^k \left(\frac{1}{2}\right)^{k-1}\left(\frac{1}{2}\right) = \left(\frac{5}{12}\right)^k$.

Now for any k, $p(k) + q(k) = \frac{1}{6}\left(\frac{5}{12}\right)^{k-1} + \left(\frac{5}{12}\right)^k = \frac{7}{12}\left(\frac{5}{12}\right)^{k-1}$.

Then $E = \sum_{k=1}^{\infty} k \cdot \frac{7}{12}\left(\frac{5}{12}\right)^{k-1} = \frac{7}{12}\sum_{k=1}^{\infty} k\left(\frac{5}{12}\right)^{k-1}$.

Let $T = \sum_{k=1}^{\infty} k\left(\frac{5}{12}\right)^{k-1}$.   [Don't panic. Take it one step at a time.]

$$T = 1 + 2\left(\frac{5}{12}\right) + 3\left(\frac{5}{12}\right)^2 + \cdots + k\left(\frac{5}{12}\right)^{k-1} + \cdots$$

$$\frac{5}{12}T = \frac{5}{12} + 2\left(\frac{5}{12}\right)^2 + \cdots + (k-1)\left(\frac{5}{12}\right)^{k-1} + \cdots$$

Subtract to give

$$\frac{7}{12}T = 1 + \frac{5}{12} + \left(\frac{5}{12}\right)^2 + \cdots + \left(\frac{5}{12}\right)^{k-1} + \cdots$$

$$= \frac{1}{1 - \frac{5}{12}} = \frac{12}{7}.$$

$$T = \left(\frac{12}{7}\right)^2.$$

Now $E = \frac{7}{12}T = \frac{12}{7}$.

Ann's expected number of rolls is $\frac{12}{7}$.

9. *Solution 1*

Let the angle between the radius OQ and the positive x-axis be θ. Then P is the point $(2\cos\theta, 2\sin\theta)$, Q is the point $(3\cos\theta, 3\sin\theta)$ and R is the point $(3\cos\theta, 2\sin\theta)$, for $0 \le \theta \le 2\pi$.

If $R(3\cos\theta, 2\sin\theta)$ lies on the ellipse with

equation $\dfrac{x^2}{9} + \dfrac{y^2}{4} = 1$, it must satisfy the equation.

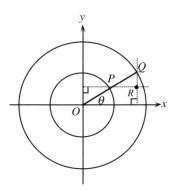

$$
\begin{aligned}
\text{LS} &= \frac{x^2}{9} + \frac{y^2}{4} \\
&= \frac{9\cos^2\theta}{9} + \frac{4\sin^2\theta}{4} \\
&= \cos^2\theta + \sin^2\theta \\
&= 1 \\
&= \text{RS}.
\end{aligned}
$$

Hence R lies on the ellipse $\dfrac{x^2}{9} + \dfrac{y^2}{4} = 1$.

Solution 2

Let the coordinates of R be (X, Y), those of P be (a, Y), and those of Q be (X, b).

Then, since P is on the inner circle, $a^2 + Y^2 = 4$, and since Q is on the outer circle, $X^2 + b^2 = 9$.

The slope of OP is $\dfrac{Y}{a}$ and the slope of OQ is $\dfrac{b}{X}$.

Since O, P and Q are collinear, $\dfrac{Y}{a} = \dfrac{b}{X}$. Hence $b = \dfrac{XY}{a}$.

Substitute into $X^2 + b^2 = 9$ to give

$$ X^2 + \frac{X^2Y^2}{a^2} = 9. $$

But $a^2 = 4 - Y^2$, and so $X^2 + \dfrac{X^2Y^2}{4 - Y^2} = 9$

$$ 4X^2 - X^2Y^2 + X^2Y^2 = 36 - 9Y^2 $$

$$ 4X^2 + 9Y^2 = 36 $$

or $$ \frac{X^2}{9} + \frac{Y^2}{4} = 1. $$

Therefore R is on the ellipse $\dfrac{x^2}{9} + \dfrac{y^2}{4} = 1$.

10.   *Solution*

(a)   Trivially, if $n=1$ we have only one placement, and for $n=1$, $2^{n-1} = 2^0 = 1$. The statement holds for $n=1$. If $n>1$ there are only two positions (position 1 or position n) for placing 1. With 1 fixed, there are only two positions available for 2, either the first empty spot or the last empty one. Similarly for $3, 4, 5, ..., n-1$. This leaves one position only for n. The number of dominating permutations is 2^{n-1}.

(b)   There are three cases:

(i)   The two 1's are split, which is possible only with one in position 1 and the other in position $(n+1)$. The remaining $(n-1)$ numbers now form 2^{n-2} dominating permutations from part (a).

(ii) The 1's are together in positions $(1, 2)$ or positions $(n-1, n)$. From part (a), in either case there are 2^{n-2} dominating permutations for the remaining numbers. Hence this case yields $2 \cdot 2^{n-2}$ dominating permutations.

(iii) The 1's are together in positions $(2, 3), (3, 4), ..., (n-2, n-1)$. [Note: It is interesting to note that cases (ii) and (iii) cannot be combined. You should satisfy yourself that they *must* be considered separately.] Hence there are k of the remaining $(n-1)$ numbers, with $1 \le k \le n-2$, preceding the pair of 1's and $(n-1-k)$ numbers following them. We have $\binom{n-1}{k}$ ways of choosing the k-set, each of which allows for 2^{k-1} dominating permutations. There are $2^{k-1}\binom{n-1}{k}$ dominating permutations for the k positions and for each of these there are $(n-1-k)$ numbers following the 11, which yields 2^{n-2-k} dominating permutations. This case, then, gives $2^{k-1}\binom{n-1}{k}2^{n-2-k} = 2^{n-3}\binom{n-1}{k}$ dominating permutations for *each k*, or a total of $\sum_{k=1}^{n-2} 2^{n-3}\binom{n-1}{k} = 2^{n-3}\sum_{k=1}^{n-2}\binom{n-1}{k}$. This sum is the sum of all coefficients in the expansion $(1+x)^{n-1}$ except for the first and last coefficients, $\binom{n-1}{0}$ and $\binom{n-1}{n-1}$, each of which is 1. Hence, since the sum of all coefficients is 2^{n-1}, we have $2^{n-3}\sum_{k=1}^{n-2}\binom{n-1}{k} = 2^{n-3}[2^{n-1}-2]$

$$= 2^{2n-4} - 2^{n-2}$$

Adding the results from the three cases, the total number of dominating permutations is $2^{n-2} + 2 \cdot 2^{n-2} + 2^{2n-4} - 2^{n-2}$ or $2^{2n-4} + 2^{n-1}$.

11. *Solution*

Since a, b, c are the roots of $x^3 + ax^2 + bx + c = 0$, then

$$x^3 + ax^2 + bx + c = (x - a)(x - b)(x - c).$$

Then $a + b + c = -a$ or $2a + b + c = 0$ (1)

$\qquad ab + bc + ca = b$ (2)

$\qquad\qquad abc = -c$ (3)

From (3) either $c = 0$ or $ab = -1$.

If $c = 0$, then (1) becomes $2a + b = 0$

and (2) becomes $ab = b$.

If $b = -2a$, $-2a^2 = -2a$

$$a^2 = a.$$

Then $a = 1$ or 0

$\qquad b = -2$ or 0.

Hence there are solutions $(0, 0, 0)$ and $(1, -2, 0)$ and no others when $c = 0$.

If $c \neq 0$, then $ab = -1$ and so $b = -\dfrac{1}{a}$, $a \neq 0$.

Now (1) becomes $2a - \dfrac{1}{a} + c = 0$, and $c = \dfrac{1 - 2a^2}{a}$.

Also (2) becomes $-1 - \dfrac{c}{a} + ca = -\dfrac{1}{a}$.

Substituting for c we obtain

$\quad 2a^4 - 2a^2 - a + 1 = 0$

or $\quad (a - 1)(2a^3 + 2a^2 - 1) = 0$.

If $a = 1$, then $b = c = -1$ and there is a solution $(1, -1, -1)$.

The remaining factor $2a^3 + 2a^2 - 1$ cannot be reduced in rationals, but there must be either one or three real roots for $2a^3 + 2a^2 - 1 = 0$.

Consider $y = 2a^3 + 2a^2 - 1$

$\quad y' = 6a^2 + 4a = 0$ if $a = 0$ or $a = -\dfrac{2}{3}$.

Hence there are two extrema. Also $y(0) = -1$ and $y\left(-\dfrac{2}{3}\right) = -\dfrac{19}{27}$.

Hence both local maximum and minimum points are below the a-axis, so we conclude that the graph of $y = 2a^3 + 2a^2 - 1$ crosses the a-axis precisely once and that there is precisely one real value of a for which $2a^3 + 2a^2 - 1 = 0$.

Thus there exists one set (a, b, c) which consists of real values (which cannot easily be determined).

We then conclude that there are four triples satisfying the given condition.

12. *Solution*

Since $\angle ADB = 2\theta$ and $\angle CDB = \angle ADE$,

$\angle CDB = \dfrac{\pi}{2} - \theta$.

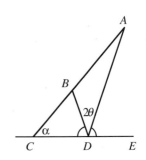

Hence $\angle A = \pi - \left(\dfrac{\pi}{2} + \theta + \alpha \right) = \dfrac{\pi}{2} - (\alpha + \theta)$.

Also $\angle CBD = \pi - \left(\alpha + \dfrac{\pi}{2} - \theta \right) = \dfrac{\pi}{2} - (\alpha - \theta)$.

Employing the Law of Sines in $\triangle CDB$,

$$\dfrac{BC}{\sin\left(\dfrac{\pi}{2} - \theta \right)} = \dfrac{CD}{\sin\left(\dfrac{\pi}{2} - (\alpha - \theta) \right)}$$

or $\qquad \dfrac{BC}{\cos\theta} = \dfrac{CD}{\cos(\alpha - \theta)}$.

Then $BC = \dfrac{CD \cos\theta}{\cos(\alpha - \theta)}$.

Similarly in $\triangle ACD$,

$$\dfrac{AC}{\sin\left(\dfrac{\pi}{2} + \theta \right)} = \dfrac{CD}{\sin\left(\dfrac{\pi}{2} - (\alpha + \theta) \right)}$$

or $\qquad AC = \dfrac{CD \cos\theta}{\cos(\alpha + \theta)}$.

Then $\dfrac{AC}{BC} = \dfrac{\cos(\alpha - \theta)}{\cos(\alpha + \theta)}$.

Now if $\dfrac{\cos(\alpha - \theta)}{\cos(\alpha + \theta)} = 2$, then $\dfrac{AC}{BC} = 2$.

Then $AC = 2BC$ and $AB = BC$.

Also if $AB = BC$, then $\dfrac{AC}{BC} = 2$ and $\dfrac{\cos(\alpha - \theta)}{\cos(\alpha + \theta)} = 2$.

Hence $AB = BC$ if and only if $\dfrac{\cos(\alpha - \theta)}{\cos(\alpha + \theta)} = 2$.

13. *Solution 1*

If $x^2 + kx = 4y^2 - 4y + 1$, then $x(x+k) = (2y-1)^2$.

Since y is an integer, then $2y - 1$ is odd and so $(2y-1)^2$ is odd.

Therefore x and $x + k$ are both odd, which means that k is even.

If x is odd, let $x = 2m - 1$ for some integer m.

Then $x^2 + kx = (2m-1)^2 + k(2m-1) = 4y^2 - 4y + 1$

$$4m^2 - 4m + 1 + k(2m-1) = 4y^2 - 4y + 1$$

$$k(2m-1) = 4[y(y-1) - m(m-1)]. \qquad (1)$$

Since $y(y-1)$ and $m(m-1)$ are both products of consecutive integers, $y(y-1)$ and $m(m-1)$ are both even.

Therefore $4[y(y-1) - m(m-1)]$ is divisible by 8.

Therefore $k(2m-1)$ is divisible by 8.

But $2m - 1$ is odd, so k must be divisible by 8.

If we can show that $k = 8$ is actually possible, then 8 is the smallest possible positive value for k.

Now, $k = 8$ is possible, since $k = 8$, $x = 1$, and $y = 2$ yields the true statement

$$1^2 + 8(1) = 4(2^2) - 4(2) + 1.$$

Therefore the smallest positive value of k is 8.

Solution 2

If $x^2 + kx = 4y^2 - 4y + 1$, then

$$x^2 + kx + \frac{k^2}{4} = 4y^2 - 4y + 1 + \frac{k^2}{4}$$

$$4x^2 + 4kx + k^2 = 16y^2 - 16y + 4 + k^2$$

$$(2x + k)^2 = k^2 + (4y - 2)^2.$$

Hence the numbers k, $4y - 2$, and $2x + k$ are integers and form a Pythagorean triple, with $4y - 2$ always even and $2x + k$ largest.

If the triple is 3, 4, 5, then $4y - 2 = 4$, which gives $y = \frac{3}{2}$, which is not an integer.

If the triple is 5, 12, 13, then $4y - 2 = 12$, which gives $y = \frac{7}{2}$, which is not an integer.

If the triple is 6, 8, 10, then $4y - 2 = 6$, $k = 8$ and $2x + k = 10$ giving $y = 2, k = 8$, and $x = 1$; or $4y - 2 = 8$ which gives $y = \frac{5}{2}$, which is not an integer.

If the triple is 7, 24, 25, then $4y - 2 = 24$, which gives $y = \frac{13}{2}$, which is not an integer.

No other triples could have k less than 8.

Therefore the smallest positive value of k is 8.

14. *Solution*
   (a) Since the perimeter is P and the equal sides are of
        length x, the third side will be $P-2x$.
        Represent the height of the triangle as h.
        Now, by Pythagoras,

$$h^2 = x^2 - \left(\frac{P-2x}{2}\right)^2$$

$$= \frac{4x^2 - P^2 + 4Px - 4x^2}{4}$$

$$= \frac{4Px - P^2}{4}.$$

$$h = \frac{\sqrt{4Px - P^2}}{2}, \ h \geq 0.$$

   Then $A(x)$, the function that describes the area for a given value of x, is

$$A(x) = \frac{1}{4}(P - 2x)\sqrt{4Px - P^2}.$$

   Since $A(x) \geq 0$, $P - 2x \geq 0$, so $x \leq \frac{P}{2}$

   and since $A(x)$ is real, $4Px - P^2 \geq 0$, so $x \geq \frac{P}{4}$.

   For real triangles $\frac{P}{4} \leq x \leq \frac{P}{2}$.

   (b) To determine the maximum value of $A(x)$ we set $A'(x) = 0$

$$A'(x) = \frac{1}{4}\left[\sqrt{4Px - P^2}(-2) + (P - 2x)\cdot\frac{1}{2}\left(4Px - P^2\right)^{-\frac{1}{2}}(4P)\right]$$

$$= \frac{1}{4}\left[\frac{2P(P - 2x)}{\sqrt{4Px - P^2}} - 2\sqrt{4Px - P^2}\right]$$

$$= \frac{1}{4}\left[\frac{2P^2 - 4Px - 8Px + 2P^2}{\sqrt{4Px - P^2}}\right].$$

$$A'(x) = \frac{P^2 - 3Px}{\sqrt{4Px - P^2}}.$$

   If $A'(x) = 0$, $P^2 - 3Px = 0$

$$x = \frac{P}{3}.$$

$$A\left(\frac{P}{4}\right) = A\left(\frac{P}{2}\right) = 0 \quad \text{and} \quad A\left(\frac{P}{3}\right) = \frac{1}{4}\left(\frac{P}{3}\right)\left(\sqrt{\frac{P^2}{3}}\right)$$

$$= \frac{P^2}{12\sqrt{3}} > 0.$$

Hence there is a maximum at $x = \frac{P}{3}$.

For the area to be an integer

$$\frac{P^2}{12\sqrt{3}} \geq 1$$

$$P^2 \geq 12\sqrt{3} \doteq 20.78.$$

The smallest value of P for which this is true is 5.

Hence we conclude $P \geq 5$, and for every value of $P \geq 5$, $A(x)$ is a continuous

function for $\frac{P}{4} \leq x \leq \frac{P}{2}$. It can achieve all integer values from 1 to $\frac{P^2}{12\sqrt{3}}$.

(c)   If $P = 20$, $\dfrac{P^2}{12\sqrt{3}} = \dfrac{400}{12\sqrt{3}}$

$$\doteq 19.24.$$

There are 19 triangles with integer area and perimeter of 20.

(d)   For $P \geq 5$ every integer value $(1, 2, 3, ...)$ can be achieved for A up to the integer

value of $\dfrac{P^2}{12\sqrt{3}}$, and the number of integer values of A is $\left\lfloor \dfrac{P^2}{12\sqrt{3}} \right\rfloor$.

15.   *Solution*

Let the coordinates of P be (x, y).

Then the locus of P is defined by

$$|x| + |y| = \sqrt{(x-1)^2 + (y-1)^2}.$$

By squaring both sides we can eliminate the radical.
(Remember that we must be careful about the absolute values.)

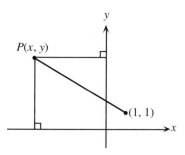

$$x^2 + 2|xy| + y^2 = x^2 - 2x + 1 + y^2 - 2y + 1$$
$$|xy| + x + y - 1 = 0 \qquad\qquad (1)$$

There are two cases to consider. First, $xy \geq 0$ (x and y both positive, i.e. P in quadrant 1, or x and y both negative, i.e. P in quadrant 3), and second, $xy \leq 0$ (x and y opposite in sign, i.e. P in quadrants 2 or 4).

Case 1: $xy \geq 0$. Then $|xy| = xy$ and statement (1) becomes

$$xy + x + y - 1 = 0$$
$$xy + x + y + 1 = 2$$
$$(x+1)(y+1) = 2$$
$$y + 1 = \frac{2}{x+1}.$$

This equation represents a hyperbola of the form

$y = \frac{2}{x}$ with asymptotes $y = -1$ and $x = -1$, but since

$xy \geq 0$ we want only the portion of the graph in
quadrants 1 and 3. The x and y intercepts are both 1.

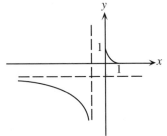

Case 2: $xy \leq 0$. Then $|xy| = -xy$ and statement (1) becomes

$$xy - x - y + 1 = 0$$
$$\text{or } (x-1)(y-1) = 0$$
and $x = 1$ or $y = 1$.

Now $x = 1$ is the equation of a straight line, but
since $x = 1$, then $y < 0$ to satisfy $xy < 0$, so we
have only that portion of the line in quadrant 4.
Similarly, $y = 1$ gives us the portion of that line
lying in quadrant 2.

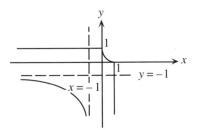

Putting these two cases together we have that
the locus of P is defined by

$$xy + x + y - 1 = 0 \text{ for } xy \geq 0$$
and $xy - x - y + 1 = 0$ for $xy \leq 0$.

16. *Solution*

Consider two limiting cases:

Case 1:   (as shown in the diagram)

Here, $x = \sqrt{6^2 + 8^2}$
         $= 10$.

For $x \geq 10$, $\angle B \geq 90°$, and so the triangle is not
acute-angled.

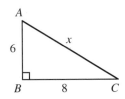

Now allow point A to move towards point C. Then $\angle A$
increases in size and $\angle B$ decreases, and we get:

Case 2:   (as shown in the diagram)

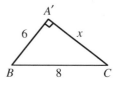

Here, $x = \sqrt{64 - 36}$

$\qquad = \sqrt{28}$

$\qquad = 2\sqrt{7}.$

For $x \leq 2\sqrt{7}$, $\angle A' \geq 90°$, and so the triangle is not acute-angled.
Therefore the triangle is acute-angled for all x such that $2\sqrt{7} < x < 10$.

17. *Solution 1*

Consider the quadrilateral as labelled.

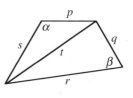

$t^2 = p^2 + s^2 - 2ps \cos \alpha$

$\qquad = q^2 + r^2 - 2qr \cos \beta.$

Then $\frac{1}{2}\left(p^2 + s^2 - q^2 - r^2\right) = ps \cos \alpha - qr \cos \beta.$

$\qquad$ (1)

If A is the area of the quadrilateral, then

$\qquad 2A = ps \sin \alpha + qr \sin \beta.$ (2)

Square (1) and (2) and add the resulting equations.

$$\frac{1}{4}\left(p^2 + s^2 - q^2 - r^2\right)^2 + 4A^2 = p^2 s^2 + q^2 r^2 - 2pqrs(\cos \alpha \cos \beta - \sin \alpha \sin \beta)$$

$$= p^2 s^2 + q^2 r^2 - 2pqrs \cos (\alpha + \beta).$$

$$16A^2 = 4p^2 s^2 + 4q^2 r^2 - \left(p^2 + s^2 - q^2 - r^2\right)^2 - 8pqrs \cos (\alpha + \beta)$$

$$= 4(ps + qr)^2 - 8pqrs - \left(p^2 + s^2 - q^2 - r^2\right)^2 - 8pqrs \cos (\alpha + \beta)$$

$$= \left[2(ps + qr)\right]^2 - \left(p^2 + s^2 - q^2 - r^2\right)^2 - 8pqrs\left[1 + \cos (\alpha + \beta)\right]$$

$$= \left(2ps + 2qr + p^2 + s^2 - q^2 - r^2\right)\left(2ps + 2qr - p^2 - s^2 + q^2 + r^2\right) - 8pqrs\left[1 + \cos (\alpha + \beta)\right]$$

$$= \left[(p + s)^2 - (q - r)^2\right]\left[(q + r)^2 - (p - s)^2\right] - 8pqrs\left[1 + \cos (\alpha + \beta)\right]$$

$$= (p + s + q - r)(p + s - q + r)(q + r + p - s)(q + r - p + s) - 8pqrs\left[1 + \cos (\alpha + \beta)\right].$$

Since the sum of any three sides of a quadrilateral is greater than the fourth and since p, q,
r, s are fixed, $(p + s + q - r)(p + s - q + r)(q + r + p - s)(q + r - p + s)$ has a fixed positive
value. Hence $16A^2$ and thus A is a maximum when $8pqrs\left[1 + \cos (\alpha + \beta)\right]$ is a minimum.
But $8pqrs$ is also fixed, so we must minimize $1 + \cos (\alpha + \beta)$.

Since $0 < \alpha + \beta < 2\pi$,

$\qquad -1 \leq \cos (\alpha + \beta) < 1.$

Hence $1 + \cos (\alpha + \beta)$ has a minimum value of 0 when $\cos (\alpha + \beta) = -1$, or when $\alpha + \beta = \pi$.
Thus the area of the quadrilateral is maximized when $\alpha + \beta = \pi$, or when the vertices lie on
a circle.

18.   *Solution 1*

Assume that there exists a single value of m where p, q, and r are all perfect squares.

Since $p = 2m - 1$, p is odd and thus p is an odd perfect square.

Hence, $p = 8k + 1$, for some integer k. [Can you prove that all odd squares are of this form?]

Thus, $2m - 1 = 8k + 1$ or $m = 4k + 1$ which is odd.

Then $r = 15m - 5$ must be an even perfect square, and since an even perfect square occurs when an even integer is squared, $15m - 5 = (2t)^2$ for some integer t.

Therefore, $15m - 5 = 15(4k + 1) - 5 = 60k + 10 = 4t^2$.

Since 4 divides $60k$ but 4 does not divide 10, it follows that there is no value of t (or of m) such that p, q, and r are all perfect squares.

[NOTE: The above solution does not involve q, but relies solely on arguments involving p and r.]

Solution 2

Every integer is of one of the forms $4k$, $4k + 1$, $4k + 2$, $4k + 3$.

Now consider $(4k)^2 = 16k^2 = 4(4k^2) = 4n$ for some integer n.

$$(4k + 1)^2 = 16k^2 + 8k + 1 = 4(4k^2 + 2k) + 1 = 4n + 1 \text{ for some integer } n$$

$$(4k + 2)^2 = 16k^2 + 16k + 4 = 4(4k^2 + 4k + 1) = 4n \text{ for some integer } n$$

$$(4k + 3)^2 = 16k^2 + 24k + 9 = 4(4k^2 + 6k + 2) + 1 = 4n + 1 \text{ for some integer } n.$$

Therefore, the squares of all integers are of the form $4n$ or $4n + 1$.

If m is of the form $4k$, then $p = 2m - 1 = 2(4k) - 1$, which is of the form $4s - 1$ (or $4s + 3$) which is not a perfect square.

If m is of the form $4k + 1$, then

$r = 15m - 5 = 15(4k + 1) - 5 = 60k + 10 = 4(15k + 2) + 2 = 4s + 2$ which is not a perfect square.

If m is of the form $4k + 2$, then $p = 2m - 1 = 2(4k + 2) - 1 = 8k + 3 = 4(2k) + 3 = 4s + 3$ which is not a perfect square.

If m is of the form $4k + 3$, then

$q = 13m - 1 = 13(4k + 3) - 1 = 52k + 38 = 4(13k + 9) + 2 = 4s + 2$ which is not a perfect square.

Therefore, there is no single value of m such that p, q, and r are perfect squares.

[NOTE: This solution can be shortened using congruence notation.]

19. *Solution*

(a) The first term is $t_1 = 4$, the common difference is $d = 3$, and the general term is
$t_n = a + (n-1)d$.
$$t_n = 4 + (n-1)(3)$$
$$= 3n + 1.$$

Now $t_5 = 16$, $t_9 = 28$ and $t_{16} = 49$.

Therefore $\dfrac{t_9}{t_5} = \dfrac{7}{4}$ and $\dfrac{t_{16}}{t_9} = \dfrac{7}{4}$.

Since $\dfrac{t_9}{t_5} = \dfrac{t_{16}}{t_9}$, then t_5, t_9 and t_{16} form a three-term geometric sequence.

(b) We find $t_{21} = 64$, $t_{37} = 112$ and $t_{65} = 196$ and so $\dfrac{t_{37}}{t_{21}} = \dfrac{7}{4} = \dfrac{t_{65}}{t_{37}}$.

Hence t_{21}, t_{37} and t_{65} form a three-term geometric sequence.

(c) Since $t_n = 3n + 1$, $t_k = 3k + 1$.

But $k = 5 + 16p$, $p = 0, 1, 2, 3, ...$, therefore $t_k = 3(16p + 5) + 1$
$$= 16 + 48p.$$

Since the common ratio is $\dfrac{7}{4}$, the second term will be $\dfrac{7}{4}t_k = 7(4 + 12p)$
$$= 28 + 84p$$
$$= 3(9 + 28p) + 1.$$

The third term is $\dfrac{7}{4} \cdot \dfrac{7}{4}t_k = 7(7 + 21p)$
$$= 49 + 147p$$
$$= 3(49p + 16) + 1.$$

The three terms forming the geometric sequence are $16 + 48p$, $28 + 84p$ and $49 + 147p$, $p = 0, 1, 2, 3, ...$ with t_k the first term and common ratio $\dfrac{7}{4}$.

Since each term can be expressed in the form $3m + 1$, each term will also be a member of the arithmetic sequence, S.

20.   *Solution 1*

Since $1\,000\,000 = 10^6 = 2^6 5^6$, the divisors are of the form $2^a 5^b$ where $a = 0, 1, 2, 3, 4,$
5, 6 and $b = 0, 1, 2, 3, 4, 5, 6$.

Therefore there are $7 \times 7 = 49$ divisors.
They are: $2^0 5^0 \quad 2^0 5^1 \quad 2^0 5^2 \quad \cdots \quad 2^0 5^6$

$$2^1 5^0 \quad 2^1 5^1 \quad 2^1 5^2 \quad \cdots \quad 2^1 5^6$$

$$\vdots \quad\quad \vdots \quad\quad \vdots \quad\quad \vdots \quad\quad \vdots$$

$$2^6 5^0 \quad 2^6 5^1 \quad 2^6 5^2 \quad \cdots \quad 2^6 5^6$$

The sum of the logarithms (base 10) of all of the divisors equals the logarithm (base 10)
of the product of all of the divisors. [i.e. if the divisors are $d_1, d_2, ..., d_{49}$, then
$\log d_1 + \log d_2 + \log d_3 + ... + \log d_{49} = \log\left(d_1 d_2 d_3 ... d_{49}\right)$].
The product of all of the divisors (row by row) in all 7 rows of the chart is:

$$\left(2^0\right)^7 5^{21} \times \left(2^1\right)^7 5^{21} \times \left(2^2\right)^7 5^{21} \times \left(2^3\right)^7 5^{21} \times \left(2^4\right)^7 5^{21} \times \left(2^5\right)^7 5^{21} \times \left(2^6\right)^7 5^{21}$$

$$= \left(2^{21}\right)^7 \left(5^{21}\right)^7$$

$$= 10^{147}.$$

Therefore the sum of the logarithms (base 10) of all the divisors of 10^6 equals
$\log_{10}\left(10^{147}\right) = 147$.

Solution 2

Since $1\,000\,000 = 10^6 = 2^6 5^6$, the divisors are of the form $2^a 5^b$ where $a = 0, 1, 2, 3, 4,$
5, 6 and $b = 0, 1, 2, 3, 4, 5, 6$.
Therefore there are $7 \times 7 = 49$ divisors, namely $d_1, d_2, d_3, ..., d_{49}$.
The sum of the logarithms (base 10) of all of the divisors equals the logarithm (base 10)
of the product of all of the divisors.
Therefore $s = \log d_1 + \log d_2 + \log d_3 + ... + \log d_{49}$

$$= \log\left(d_1 d_2 d_3 ... d_{49}\right).$$

Now the 49 divisors can be grouped into 24 pairs of the form $2^a 5^b$ and $2^{6-a} 5^{6-b}$, (e.g.,
$2^0 5^0$ and $2^6 5^6$, $2^0 5^1$ and $2^6 5^5$, $2^0 5^2$ and $2^6 5^4$, ...), each of whose product is
$2^a 5^b \times 2^{6-a} 5^{6-b} = 2^6 5^6 = 10^6$, and one remaining divisor, $2^3 5^3 = 10^3$.

Therefore $s = \log\left[\left(d_1 d_{49}\right)\left(d_2 d_{48}\right)\left(d_3 d_{47}\right)\cdots\left(d_{24} d_{26}\right)\left(d_{25}\right)\right]$

$$= \log\underbrace{\left[10^6.10^6.10^6 \ldots 10^6.10^3\right]}_{\text{24 factors of } 10^6}$$

$$= \log\left[\left(10^6\right)^{24} \cdot 10^3\right]$$

$$= \log 10^{147}$$

$$= 147.$$

Therefore the sum of the logarithm (base 10) of all of the divisors of 10^6 equals 147.